S0-AUX-776

The Call to Praise

A Hymnal
For Children's Division

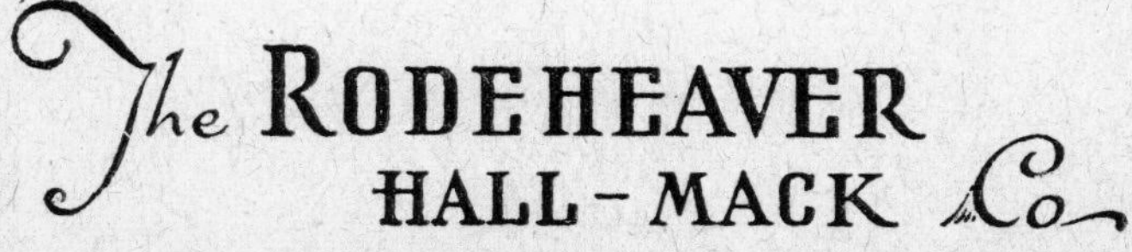
The RODEHEAVER
HALL-MACK Co.

WINONA LAKE, INDIANA

PREFACE

THE CALL TO PRAISE will surely appeal to, and receive the approval of, those interested in the spiritual growth and development of the young.

It is the result of prolonged research; it represents the combined effort and best judgment of capable teachers of the young; it is a hymnal for constant use and not for reference.

Its object is to prepare children for entrance into their church so that they may join heartily in the singing of the hymns and take an active part in worship.

Each hymn is assigned to a division. The letter under the title

B—Beginner
P—Primary
J—Junior

serves as a suggestion only, and not a restriction. Conditions vary, so that an arbitrary classification is not practicable.

Our thanks are due to Mrs. Maud Junkin Baldwin, B.R.E., for permission to adapt certain WORSHIP PROGRAMS to this work; to Miss Mabel Elsie Locker, B.R.E., and Miss Lillian E. Reed, B.R.E., for many valuable suggestions, criticisms and editorial work in the preparation of the book. Their valuable assistance is acknowledged with grateful appreciation.

THE PUBLISHERS.

The following division of the contents will be found helpful:

Call to Worship	Numbers	1	to	18
Sentences	Numbers	19	to	38
Closing Worship	Numbers	39	to	48
God—the Creator	Numbers	49	to	60
God's Word	Numbers	61	to	67
God's Care and Love	Numbers	68	to	77
The Lord Jesus	Numbers	78	to	101
Prayer	Numbers	102	to	114
Service	Numbers	115	to	126
Decision	Numbers	127	to	132
Songs with Action	Numbers	133	to	138
Missions	Numbers	139	to	145
The Church	Numbers	146	to	148
Giving Hymns	Numbers	149	to	152
The Holy Spirit	Numbers	153	to	154
God in Nature	Numbers	155	to	162
The Weather	Numbers	163	to	168
Worship and Praise	Numbers	169	to	183
Christmas	Numbers	184	to	196
Easter	Numbers	197	to	200
Harvest and Thanksgiving	Numbers	201	to	205
National	Numbers	206	to	209

The Call to Praise.

THE CALL TO WORSHIP.

This is the Day. 1

(P–J.) C. Austin Miles.

ADESTE FIDELES.

This is the day which the Lord hath made, We will re - joice and be glad in it. O come and let us wor - ship, O come and let us wor - ship, O come and let us wor - ship Christ the Lord! A - men.

Bless the Lord, O My Soul. 2

(P–J.) C. Austin Miles.

Bless the Lord, O my soul, and all that is with - in me, Bless His ho - ly name. A-men.

3 Morning Praise.
(J.)
Sir JOSEPH BARNBY.
1. When morn - ing gilds the skies, My heart a - wak - ing cries
2. When - e'er the sweet church bell Peals o - ver hill and dell
May Je - sus Christ be praised. A - like at work and pray'r,
May Je - sus Christ be praised! O hark to what it sings,
To Je - sus I re - pair; May Je - sus Christ be praised!
As joy - ous - ly it rings, May Je - sus Christ be praised! A - men.
4 Gentle Saviour, God of Love.
(P.)
Rev. J. B. DYKES.
1. Gen - tle Sav - iour, God of love, Hear us from Thy throne a - bove,
2. May the les - sons taught to - day Find us read - y to o - bey;
While we meet to praise Thee here, In our Sun - day School so dear.
Make us what we ought to be, Lead Thy chil - dren, Lord, to Thee. A - men.

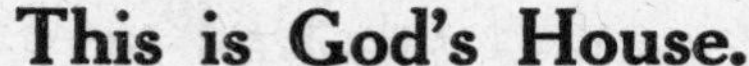

This is God's House. 5

A. A. P. (J.) A. A. Payn.

This is God's house, It is His tem - ple fair, We
know that He is here For God is ev - 'ry - where. A-men.

Holy, Holy, Holy. 6

Reginald Heber. (J.) John B. Dykes.

1. Ho - ly, ho - ly, ho - ly! Lord God Al-might - y! Ear - ly in the morn - ing our song shall rise to Thee: Ho - ly, ho - ly, ho - ly, mer - ci - ful and might - y, God in Three Per-sons, bless-ed Trin - i - ty!
2. Ho - ly, ho - ly, ho - ly! all the saints a - dore Thee, Cast - ing down their gold - en crowns a - round the glass - y sea; Cher - u - bim and sera - phim falling down be - fore Thee, Which wert, and art, and ev - er-more shalt be.
3. Ho - ly, ho - ly, ho - ly! tho' the dark-ness hide Thee, Tho' the eye of sin - ful man Thy glo - ry may not see; On - ly Thou art ho - ly, there is none be - side Thee, Per - fect in pow'r, in love, and pu - ri - ty. A-men.

7
The Earth is Hushed in Silence.
Anon.
(J.)
Felix Mendelssohn.
1. The earth is hushed in si - lence, Its cares now flee a - way;
2. The bells are sweet - ly ring - ing, Their clear - toned voic - es say:
3. Come, all ye thank - ful peo - ple! Why should our hearts de - lay
Let all things bow in rev - erence On this the Lord's own day.
Ye peo - ple, come and wor - ship On this the Lord's own day.
To greet the Lord of heav - en On this His ho - ly day?
Refrain.
O praise and pray on this, the Lord's own day! A - men.
8
O Day of Rest and Gladness.
Bishop Christopher Wordsworth.
(J.)
Berthold Tours.
1. O day of rest and glad - ness, O day of joy and light,
2. New grac - es ev - er gain - ing From this our day of rest,
O balm of care and sad - ness, Most beau - ti - ful, most bright;
We reach the rest re - main - ing To spir - its of the blest.

O Day of Rest and Gladness.
On thee the high and low - ly, Through a - ges joined in tune,
To Ho - ly Ghost be prais - es, To Fa - ther and to Son;
Sing ho - ly, ho - ly, ho - ly, To the great God Tri - une.
The Church her voice up - rais - es To Thee, blest Three in One. A - men.
Father in Heaven.
9
(P.)
LOWELL MASON.
1. Fa - ther in heav - en, bless Thy lit - tle chil - dren Gath - ered be -
2. Fa - ther in heav - en, help Thy lit - tle chil - dren To please Thee
fore Thee on Thy ho - ly day. For morn - ing sun - shine, for the day we
ev - er in their work and play. Help them be truth - ful, gen - tle, kind and
thank Thee: O Sun of love, shine in our hearts, we pray.
lov - ing, To be like Je - sus, serv - ing Him al - way. A - men.

10
Children in the Temple.
GRACE GORDON.
(P.)
ARTHUR WILTON.
1. Chil - dren in the tem - ple, Prais - ing Christ the Lord, Hark the glad ho - san - nas, Ring in sweet ac - cord!
2. Chil - dren in the tem - ple, We would join your praise, Hap - py hearts and voic - es, To the Sav - iour raise!
REFRAIN.
Praise Him! Praise Him! Glad ho - san - nas sing; Praise Him! Praise Him! Christ, the chil - dren's King! A - men.
Copyright, MCMXXIX, by Hall-Mack Co. International Copyright Secured.
11
O Give Thanks Unto the Lord.
(J.)
A. A. PAYN.
O give thanks un - to the Lord for He is good,
For His mer - cy en - dur - eth for - ev - er. A - men.
Copyright, MCMXXIX, by Hall-Mack Co. International Copyright Secured.

Call to Worship. 12

MATTIE B. SHANNON. (J.) GRACE L. HOSMER.

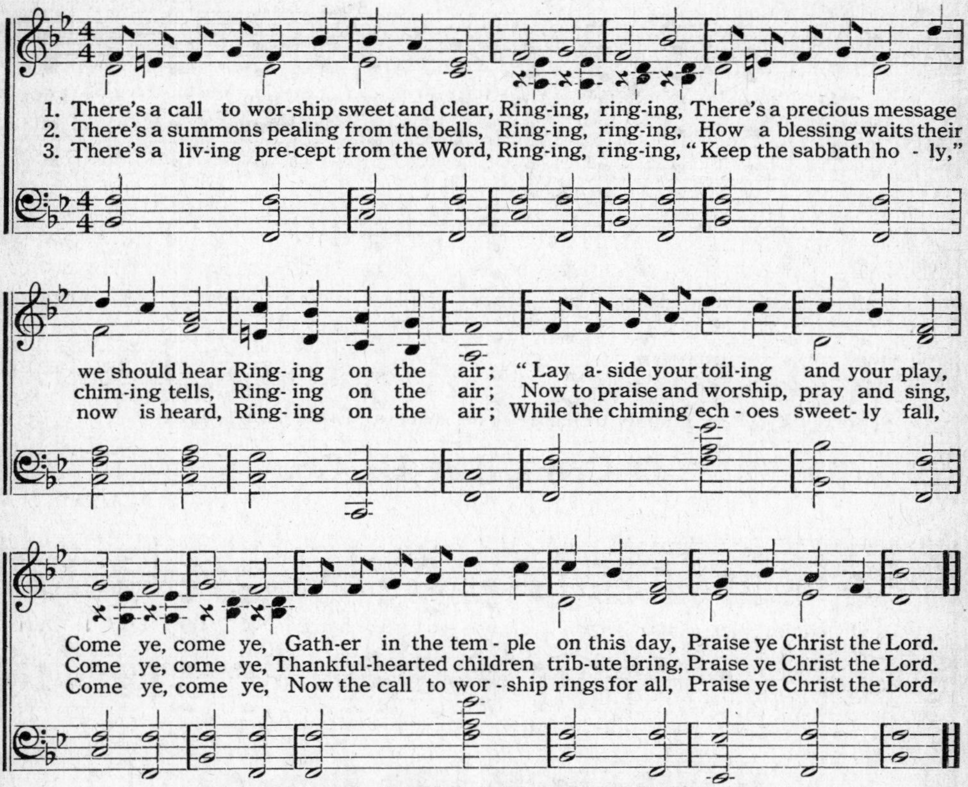

1. There's a call to wor-ship sweet and clear, Ring-ing, ring-ing, There's a precious message
2. There's a summons pealing from the bells, Ring-ing, ring-ing, How a blessing waits their
3. There's a liv-ing pre-cept from the Word, Ring-ing, ring-ing, "Keep the sabbath ho - ly,"

we should hear Ring- ing on the air; "Lay a- side your toil-ing and your play,
chim-ing tells, Ring- ing on the air; Now to praise and worship, pray and sing,
now is heard, Ring- ing on the air; While the chiming ech - oes sweet- ly fall,

Come ye, come ye, Gath-er in the tem- ple on this day, Praise ye Christ the Lord.
Come ye, come ye, Thankful-hearted children trib-ute bring, Praise ye Christ the Lord.
Come ye, come ye, Now the call to wor - ship rings for all, Praise ye Christ the Lord.

The Lord is in His Holy Temple. 13

(P–J.) WM. J. KIRKPATRICK.

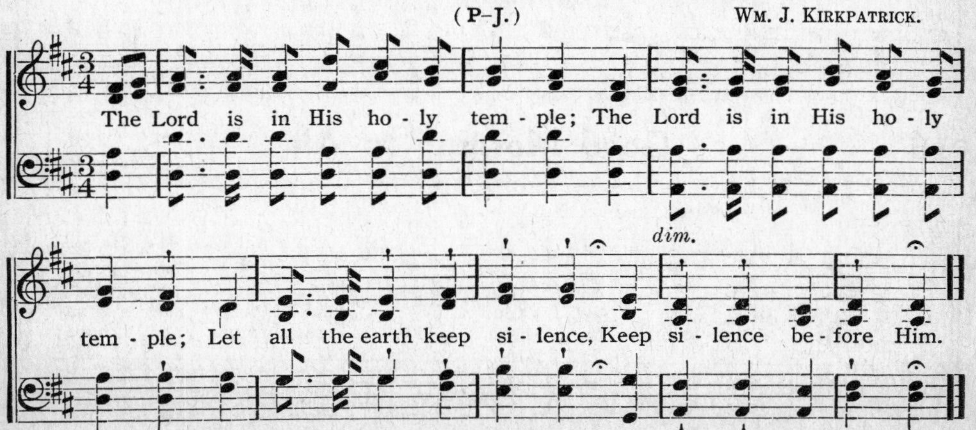
The Lord is in His ho-ly tem-ple; The Lord is in His ho-ly
dim.
tem-ple; Let all the earth keep si-lence, Keep si-lence be-fore Him.

14 In His Holy Temple.
(P–J.)
A. A. PAYN.
Slowly.
The Lord is in His ho - ly tem - ple, Let
all the earth keep si - lence be - fore Him. A - men.
Copyright, MCMXXIX, by Hall-Mack Co. International Copyright Secured.
15 O Come, Let Us Go.
(J.)
A. A. PAYN.
O come, let us go in - to the house of the Lord Our
feet shall stand with - in Thy gates, O Je - ru - sa - lem. A - men.
Copyright, MCMXXIX, by Hall-Mack Co. International Copyright Secured.
16 Good Morning to All.
(To be sung standing.)
(B–P.)
Brightly.
1. Good morn - ing to you, Good morn - ing to you,
2. We're glad to see you, We're glad to see you,
3. 'Tis love brings us here, 'Tis love brings us here;

Good Morning to All.

Good morn - ing, dear chil - dren, Good morn - ing to all;
Good morn - ing, dear chil - dren, We're glad to see you.
Re - mem - ber, dear chil - dren, 'Tis love brings us here.

This is the Day Which the Lord Hath Made. 17

(P–J.)

C. Austin Miles.

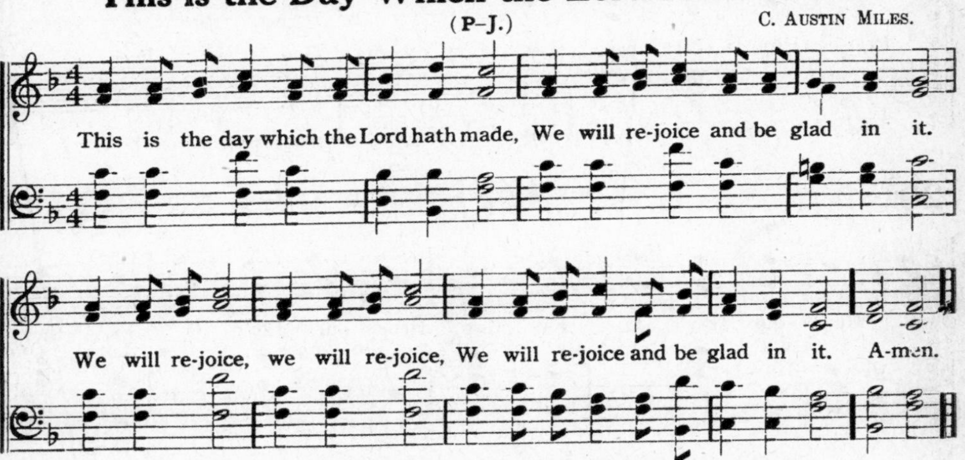
This is the day which the Lord hath made, We will re-joice and be glad in it.
We will re-joice, we will re-joice, We will re-joice and be glad in it. A-men.

Father, Hear Us When We Pray. 18

(J.)

Adam Geibel.

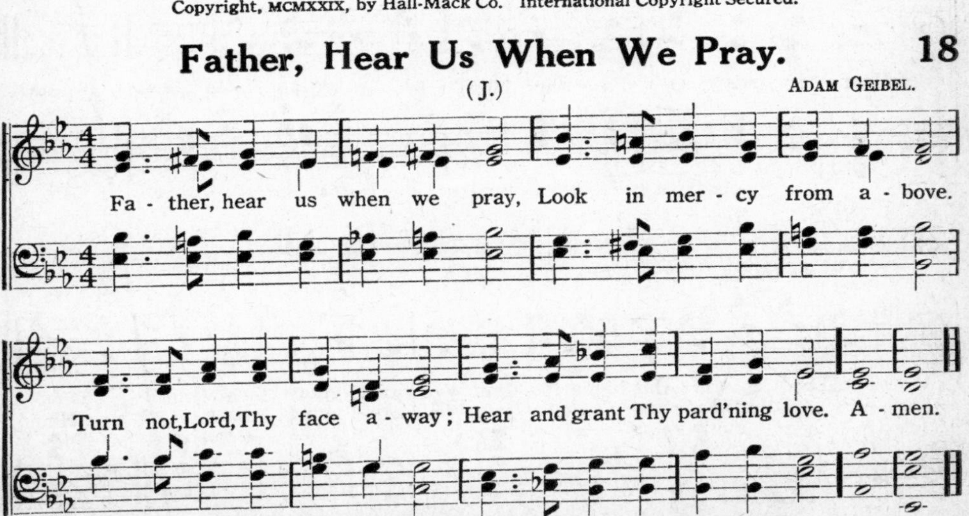
Fa - ther, hear us when we pray, Look in mer - cy from a - bove.
Turn not, Lord, Thy face a - way; Hear and grant Thy pard'ning love. A - men.

SENTENCES.

19
(B.)
C. AUSTIN MILES.
Praise Him, chil - dren ev - 'ry - where, God is near,
Praise Him, chil - dren ev - 'ry - where, God is here.
20
(P–J.)
C. A. M.
Hear our pray'r, O Fa - ther, Hear our pray'r, O Fa - ther,
Hear our pray'r, O Fa - ther, Thro' Je - sus Christ our Lord. A-men.
21
M. E. L.
(B.)
C. A. M.
1
2
The Lord is in this home to - day, We love Him, we love Him.
We bow our heads and glad - ly say, We love Him, we (Omit.........) love Him.

M. E. L.
(B.)
C. A. M.
22
God, our Fa - ther cares for us, Thank Him, thank Him,
God, our Fa - ther cares for us, * Thank Him ev - 'ry day.
* Use "Serve," "Praise," "Love."
M. E. L.
(B–P.)
C. A. M.
23
Dear Fa - ther, we thank Thee for Je - sus our Friend; Dear
Fa - ther, we thank Thee for all Thou dost send. A - men.
M. E. L.
(B.)
C. A. M.
24
Fa - ther, we thank Thee for our * mother dear, We thank Thee, we thank Thee.

* Use also, Teacher, father, sister, etc.

25 Mabel E. Locker. (B-P.) C. A. M.
Dear Je - sus, I love Thee and pray Thee to keep me
Close to Thee al - ways, a - wake or a - sleep. A - men.
26 John 15: 12. (P-J.) Clyde Willard.
Love one an - oth - er, as I have loved you.
27 John 4: 19. (P-J.) C. W.
We love Him, we love Him, be - cause He first loved us.
28 (B.) C. A. M.
This is God's house, we are His children dear, We love to pray and sing, For God is here.

29
(B.)
C. A. M.
"Suf - fer lit - tle chil- dren to come un - to me, and for - bid them not."
30
(B.)
C. A. M.
We love Je-sus, because He first lov'd us, We love Je- sus, because He first lov'd us.
31
Matthew 5: 8.
(J.)
C. W.
Bless - ed are the pure in heart; for they shall see God.
32
Psalm 23: 1.
(J.)
C. W.
The Lord is my shep - herd; I shall not want.
33
M. E. L.
(B.)
C. A. M.
Fa - ther, hear our songs to - day, Bless us as to Thee we pray. A - men.

34
(J.)
C. W.
Do un - to oth - ers as ye would that they should do un - to you.
35 Exod. 15 : 2.
(J.)
C. W.
The Lord is my strength, my strength and song, And He is be-come my sal - va - tion.
36 Isaiah 12 : 2.
(J.)
C. W.
God is my sal - va - tion, I will trust and not be a - fraid.
37 Ecclesiastes 12 : 1.
(J.)
C. W.
Re - mem - ber now thy Cre - a - tor In the days of thy youth.
38 Matthew 6 : 28.
(J.)
C. W.
Con - sid - er the lil - ies of the field, how they grow.

CLOSING WORSHIP.
Parting Prayer.
39
MABEL E. LOCKER.
(P-J.)
C. AUSTIN MILES.
Bless us and keep us, Lord, we pray, As to our homes we go......
Help us to serve Thee ev - 'ry day, And more like Thee to grow. A - men.
Copyright, MCMXXIX, by Hall-Mack Co. International Copyright Secured.
Day is Done.
40
Arr. by Rev. SAMUEL D. PRICE, D. D.
Day is done, Gone the sun, From the lake, from the hills;
From the sky, All is well, Safe - ly rest, God is nigh.
Good-Bye Hymn.
41
(P.)
Hymnal Companion.
O Lord, our hearts would give Thee praise, Ere now our school we end,
For this Thy day, the best of days, Je - sus, the children's Friend. A - men.
15

42 God, That Made the Earth and Heaven.

Bishop Reginald Heber.
Rev. William Mercer.
(J.)
Welsh Traditional Melody.
Harmonized by L. O. Emerson.
1. God, that made the earth and heav - en, Dark - ness and light;
2. And when morn a - gain shall call us To run life's way,
Who the day for toil hast giv - en, For rest the night;
May we still, what - e'er be - fall us, Thy will o - bey.
May Thine an - gel guards de - fend us, Slum - ber sweet Thy mer - cy send us;
From the pow'r of e - vil hide us, In the nar - row path-way guide us,
Ho - ly dreams and hopes at - tend us, This live - long night.
Nor Thy smile be e'er de - nied us The live - long day. A- men.
43 Good-Bye and God be With You.
John R. Clements.
(B–P.)
C. Austin Miles.
1. Good - bye and God be with you; Good - bye and God be with you;

Good-Bye and God be With You.

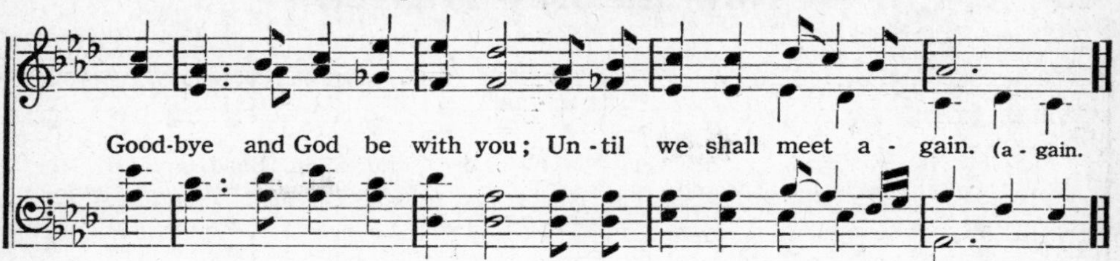
Good-bye and God be with you; Un-til we shall meet a - gain. (a - gain.

Day is Dying in the West. 44

MARY A. LATHBURY. (J.) WILLIAM F. SHERWIN.

1. Day is dy - ing in the west, Heav'n is touch-ing earth with rest; Wait and
2. Lord of life, be - neath the dome Of the u - ni - verse, Thy home, Gath - er
3. While the deep'ning shadows fall, Heart of Love, en - fold - ing all, Thro' the
4. When for - ev - er from our sight Pass the stars, the day, the night, Lord of

wor - ship while the night Sets her eve- ning lamps a-light Thro' all the sky.
us who seek Thy face To the fold of Thy embrace, For Thou art nigh.
glo - ry and the grace Of the stars that veil Thy face, Our hearts as - cend.
an - gels, on our eyes Let e - ter - nal morn-ing rise, And shad - ows end.

REFRAIN.

Ho - ly, ho - ly, ho - ly, Lord God of Hosts! Heav'n and earth are

full of Thee, Heav'n and earth are praising Thee, O Lord most high! A - men.

45 (First Tune.) Now the Day Is Over.

SABINE BARING-GOULD. (J.) C. AUSTIN MILES.

1. Now the day is o - ver, Night is draw - ing nigh, Shad - ows of the eve - ning Steal a - cross the sky. 2. Je - sus, give the wea - ry Calm and sweet re - pose; With Thy ten - d'rest bless - ing May mine eye - lids close.
3. Thro' the long night watch - es May Thine an - gels spread Their white wings a - bove me, Watch - ing round my bed. 4. When the morning wak - ens, Then may I a - rise Pure, and fresh, and sin - less In Thy ho - ly eyes. A - men.
Copyright, MCMXXIX, by Hall-Mack Co. International Copyright Secured.
46 (Second Tune.) Now the Day Is Over.
SABINE BARING-GOULD. (J.) JOSEPH BARNBY.
1. Now the day is o - ver, Night is draw - ing nigh;......
Shad - ows of the eve - ing Steal a - cross the sky. A - men.

Saviour, Again to Thy Dear Name. 47

JOHN ELLERTON. (J.) EDWARD J. HOPKINS.

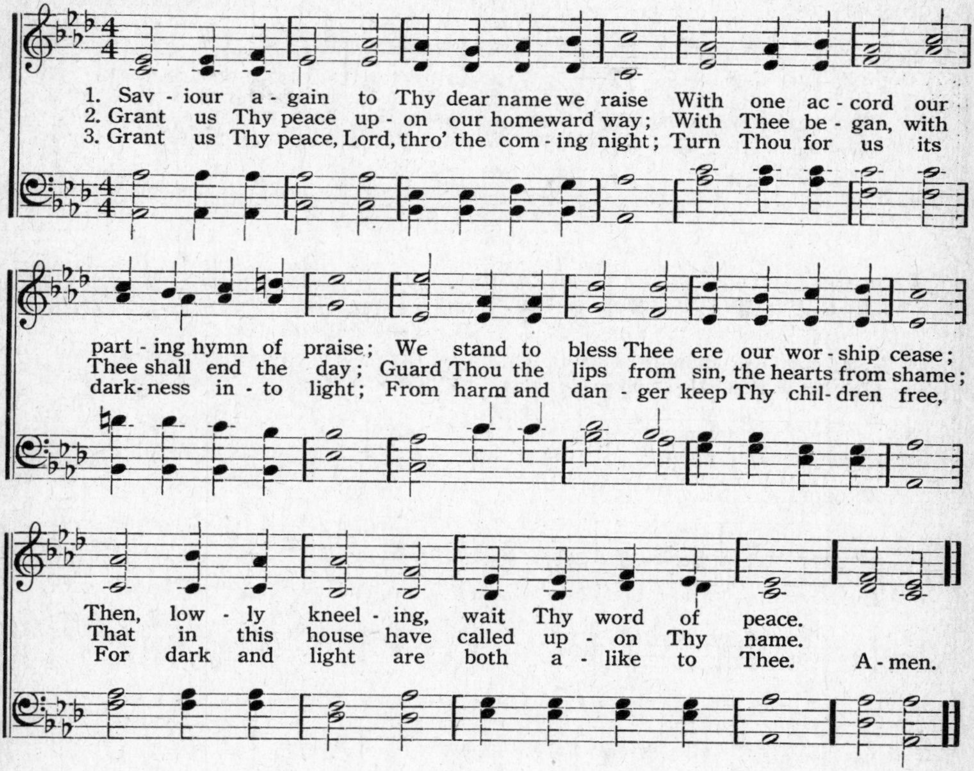

1. Sav - iour a - gain to Thy dear name we raise With one ac - cord our
2. Grant us Thy peace up - on our homeward way; With Thee be - gan, with
3. Grant us Thy peace, Lord, thro' the com - ing night; Turn Thou for us its

part - ing hymn of praise; We stand to bless Thee ere our wor - ship cease;
Thee shall end the day; Guard Thou the lips from sin, the hearts from shame;
dark - ness in - to light; From harm and dan - ger keep Thy chil - dren free,

Then, low - ly kneel - ing, wait Thy word of peace.
That in this house have called up - on Thy name.
For dark and light are both a - like to Thee. A - men.

Good-Bye Song. 48

(B.) TEACHER.

Our Sun-day-school is o - ver, And we are go - ing home. Good - bye, good - bye,

SCHOLARS.

Be al - ways kind and true. Good - bye, good - bye, We will be kind and true.

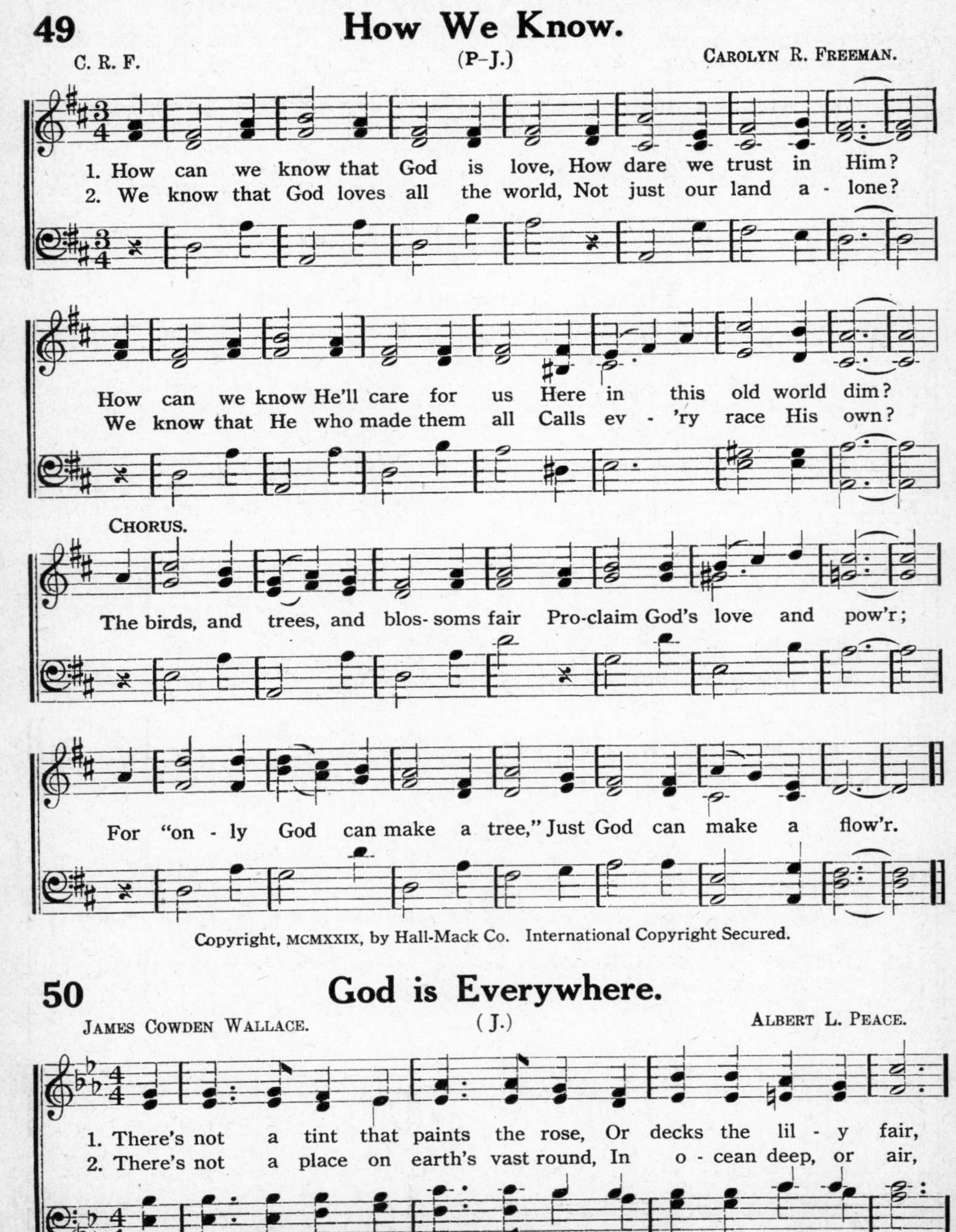
49
How We Know.
C. R. F.
(P–J.)
Carolyn R. Freeman.
1. How can we know that God is love, How dare we trust in Him?
2. We know that God loves all the world, Not just our land a - lone?
How can we know He'll care for us Here in this old world dim?
We know that He who made them all Calls ev - 'ry race His own?
Chorus.
The birds, and trees, and blos- soms fair Pro-claim God's love and pow'r;
For "on - ly God can make a tree," Just God can make a flow'r.
Copyright, MCMXXIX, by Hall-Mack Co. International Copyright Secured.
50
God is Everywhere.
James Cowden Wallace.
(J.)
Albert L. Peace.
1. There's not a tint that paints the rose, Or decks the lil - y fair,
2. There's not a place on earth's vast round, In o - cean deep, or air,

God is Everywhere.

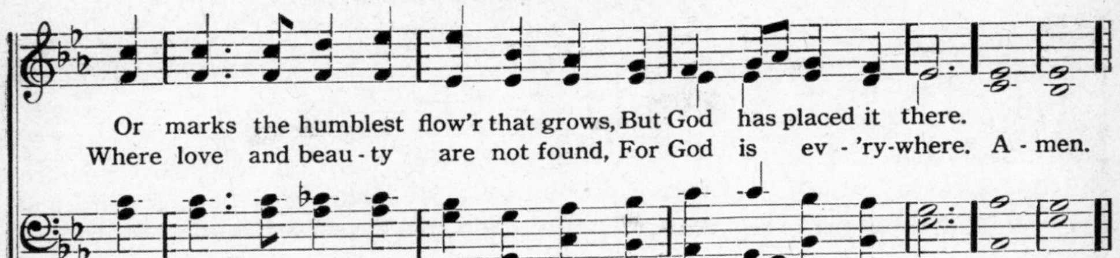
Or marks the humblest flow'r that grows, But God has placed it there.
Where love and beau - ty are not found, For God is ev - 'ry-where. A - men.

All Things Great and Wonderful. 51

C. R. F. (P.) CAROLYN R. FREEMAN.

1. All things great and won - der - ful, Come from God a - bove;
All things good and beau - ti - ful Tell us of His love.

2. Birds and sun - beams, skies of blue, Mead - ows bright with flow'rs,
God has sent to make us glad Through the fleet - ing hours.

CHORUS.

Beau - ti - ful world, won - der - ful world, Show - ing ev - 'ry - where,
How won - der - ful is God a - bove Who keeps us safe in His care.

52 Only God Can Make a Blossom.

C. R. F. (J.) CAROLYN R. FREEMAN.

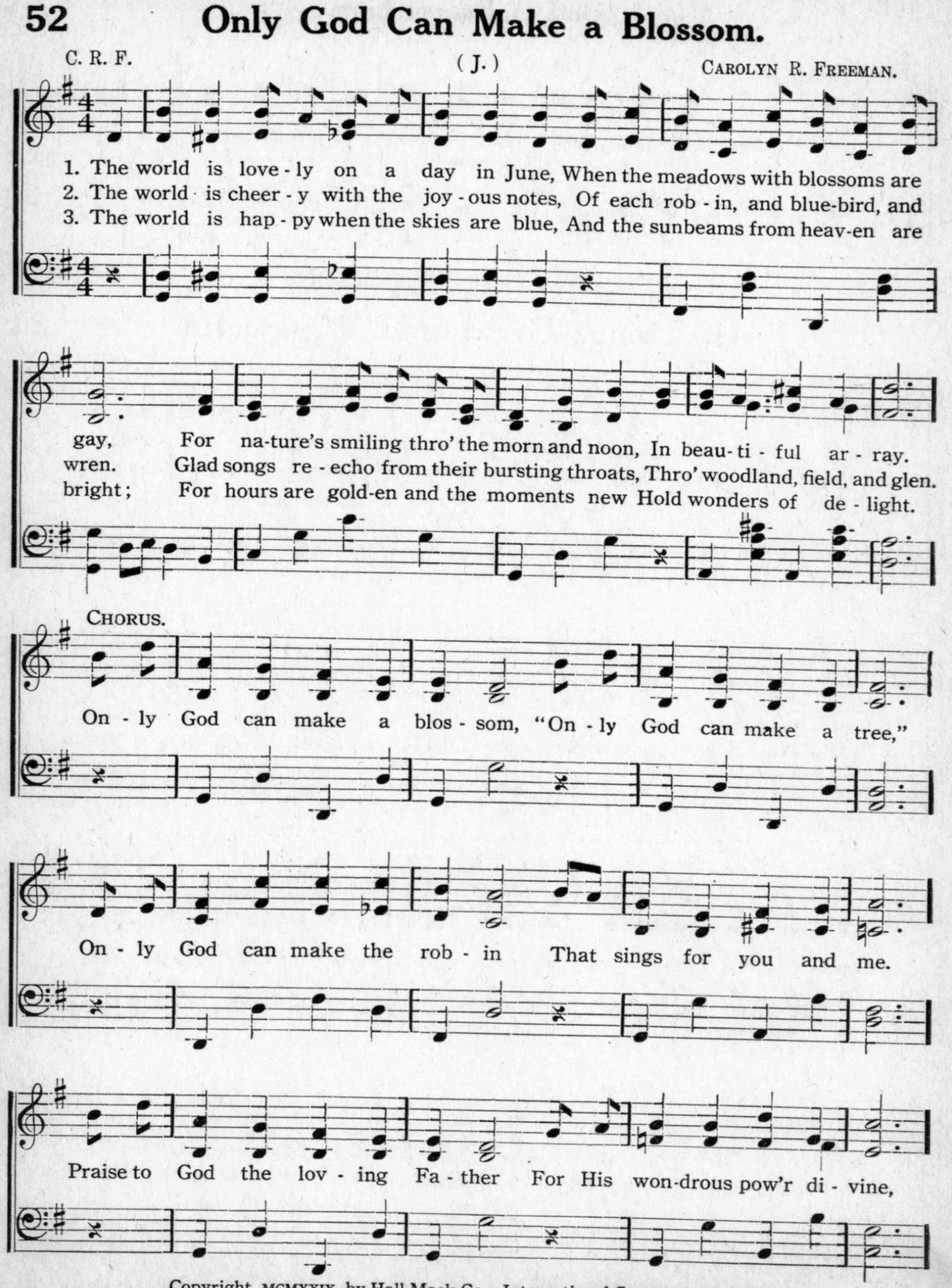
1. The world is love-ly on a day in June, When the meadows with blossoms are gay, For na-ture's smiling thro' the morn and noon, In beau-ti-ful ar-ray.
2. The world is cheer-y with the joy-ous notes, Of each rob-in, and blue-bird, and wren. Glad songs re-echo from their bursting throats, Thro' woodland, field, and glen.
3. The world is hap-py when the skies are blue, And the sunbeams from heav-en are bright; For hours are gold-en and the moments new Hold wonders of de-light.
CHORUS.
On-ly God can make a blos-som, "On-ly God can make a tree,"
On-ly God can make the rob-in That sings for you and me.
Praise to God the lov-ing Fa-ther For His won-drous pow'r di-vine,

Only God Can Make a Blossom.

For the bless-ings He has giv-en, In glad sum-mer-time.
53
This is God's World.
G. L. H.
(P-J.)
Grace L. Hosmer.
Teacher.
Response.
1. O the bright and ra-diant day! This is God's world,
2. See the crim-son sun-set sky! This is God's world,
T.
R.
Bird and leaf and blos-som say "This is God's world;"
Far and wide the ech-oes fly "This is God's world;"
T.
And the Fa-ther made it glow For His chil-dren here be-low;
Who could form the sea and land But a wise and might-y hand?
R.
Made the winds that whis-per low, "This is God's world."
Sings the o-cean to the strand "This is God's world."

54 God is Great and Good.
MATTIE B. SHANNON.
(J.)
M. ISABELLE RITTER.
1. Clouds with rain for the mead - ows, Trees with sweet cooling shade,......
2. Seas which tell of His great - ness, Winds that ech - o a call,.........
3. Night with stars in the heav - ens, Day with bright gleaming sun,.........
Birds that car - ol so gai - ly, By God were made.
Hearts of chil-dren that praise Him, God made them all.
Fruit and grain and the flow - ers, God made each one.
CHORUS.
God is great, God is good; God rules o - ver all;.........
All the day and all the night, Will hear our call.........
Copyright, MCMXXIX, by Hall-Mack Co. International Copyright Secured.
55 There's Not a Tint That Paints the Rose.
J. C. WALLACE.
(P–J.)
C. AUSTIN MILES.
1. There's not a tint that paints the rose, Or decks the lil - y fair, Or
2. There's not a star whose twinkling light Shines on the dis - tant earth, And
3. A- round, be - neath, be - low, a bove As far as space ex - tends, There
Copyright, MCMXXIX, by Hall-Mack Co. International Copyright Secured.

There's Not a Tint That Paints The Rose.
streaks the hum- blest flow'r that blows, But God has plac'd it there.
cheers the si - lent gloom of night, But God has giv'n it birth.
He dis - plays His boundless love, And pow'r with mer - cy blends. A - men.
All Things Bright and Beautiful.
56
Cecil Frances Alexander.
(P–J.)
Adapted from a Danish Folk-song.
1. Each lit - tle flow'r that o - pens, Each lit - tle bird that sings,
2. The cold winds in the win - ter, The pleas - ant sum - mer sun,
3. He gave us eyes to see them, And lips that we might tell
God made their glow - ing col - ors, He made their ti - ny wings.
The ripe fruits in the gar - den,—He made them ev - 'ry one.
The good - ness of the Fa - ther, Who do - eth all things well.
Refrain.
Yes, all things bright and beau - ti - ful, All crea - tures great and small,
And all things wise and won - der - ful, The Lord God made them all.

57
For the Beauty of the Earth.
FOLLIOTT S. PIERPONT.
(J.)
CONRAD KOCHER.
1. For the beau - ty of the earth, For the beau - ty of the skies,
For the love which from our birth O - ver and a - round us lies;
2. For the beau - ty of each hour Of the day and of the night,
Hill and vale, and tree and flow'r Sun and moon, and stars of light;
3. For the joy of hu - man love, Broth - er, sis - ter, par - ent child,
Friends on earth, and friends a - bove, For all gen - tle tho'ts and mild;
REFRAIN.
Lord of all, to Thee we raise This our hymn of grate - ful praise. A - men.
58
O Worship the King.
SIR ROBERT GRANT.
(J.)
HAYDN.
1. O wor - ship the King all - glo - rious a - bove, And grate - ful - ly
2. O tell of His might, and sing of His grace, Whose robe is the
3. Thy boun - ti - ful care what tongue can re - cite? It breathes in the
4. Frail chil - dren of dust, and fee - ble as frail, In Thee do we
sing His won - der - ful love; Our Shield and de - fend - er, the An - cient of
light whose can - o - py space; His char - iots of wrath the deep thun - der-clouds
air, it shines in the light, It streams from the hills, it de - scends to the
trust, nor find Thee to fail: Thy mer - cies how ten - der! How firm to the

O Worship the King.
days, Pa - vil - ioned in splen - dor, and gird - ed with praise.
form, And dark is His path on the wings of the storm.
plain, And sweet - ly dis - tills in the dew and the rain.
end! Our Mak - er, De - fend - er. Re - deem - er, and Friend. A - men.
This is My Father's World.
59
Rev. MALTBIE D. BABCOCK.
Traditional English Melody. Arr. by S. F. L.
1. This is my Fa - ther's world, And to my list - 'ning ears, All
2. This is my Fa - ther's world, The birds their car - ols raise, The
3. This is my Fa - ther's world, O let me ne'er for - get That
FINE.
na - ture sings and round me rings The mu - sic of the spheres.
morn - ing light, the lil - y white, De - clare their Mak - er's praise.
though the wrong seems oft so strong, God is the Rul - er yet.
D.S.—rocks and trees, of skies and seas—His hand the won - ders wrought.
D.S.—rust - ling grass I hear Him pass, He speaks to me ev - 'ry - where.
D.S.—sus who died shall be sat - is - fied, And earth and heav - en be one.
D.S.
This is my Fa - ther's world, I rest me in the thought Of
This is my Fa - ther's world, He shines in all that's fair: In the
This is my Fa - ther's world, The bat - tle is not done, Je -

Words from *Thoughts for Every Day Living*. Copyright, 1901, by Charles Scribner's Sons. Arrangement Copy right, 1915, by the Trustees of The Presbyterian Board of Publication and Sabbath School Work. Used by permission.

60 God of the Whole Wide World.

C. R. F. (P.) CAROLYN R. FREEMAN.

1. The lit - tle birds wake up and sing Their hap - py roun - de - lay, And thank the Lord for ev - 'ry - thing He gives them ev - 'ry day.
2. The brook - lets chat - ter on their way To join the deep blue sea; And all the while they seem to say, "God's been so good to me."
3. Each but - ter - fly and fra - grant breeze Pro - claim God's won - ders, too, They mur - mur to the leaf - y trees Of ev - 'ry bless - ing new.
CHORUS.
Praise, sing praise Un - to God a - bove; Praise, sing praise For the Fa - ther's ten - der love; Praise, sing praise For His gifts so full and free. God is God of the whole wide world, And shall for - ev - er be.

Who Would Not Love the Bible? 61

E. PAXTON HOOD. (P–J.) SAMUEL S. WESLEY.

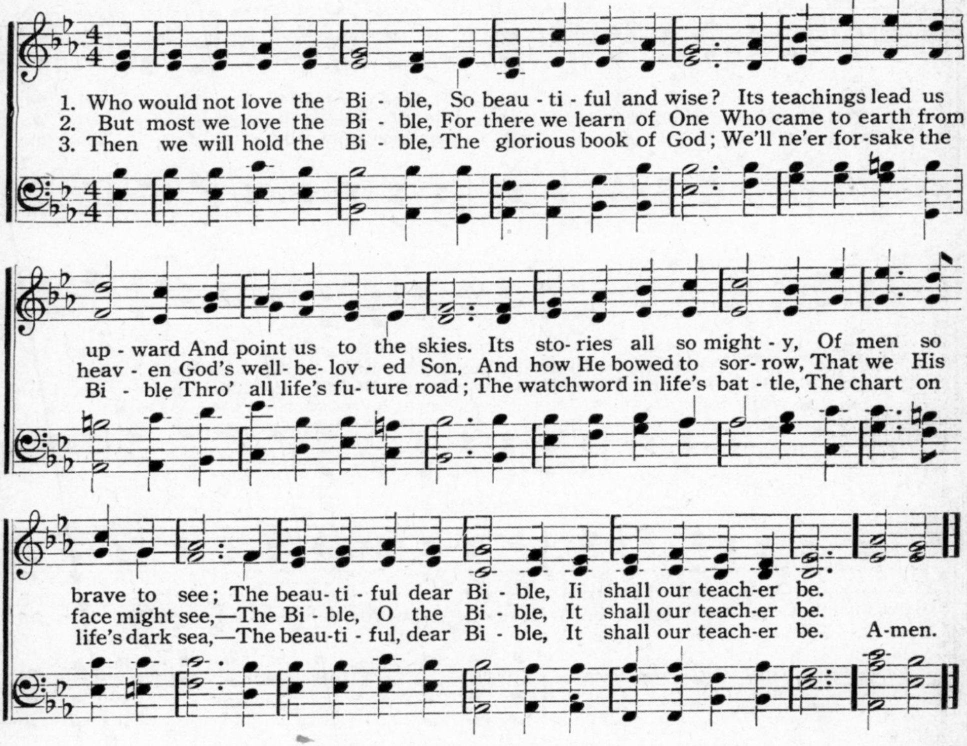

1. Who would not love the Bi - ble, So beau - ti - ful and wise? Its teachings lead us
2. But most we love the Bi - ble, For there we learn of One Who came to earth from
3. Then we will hold the Bi - ble, The glorious book of God; We'll ne'er for-sake the

up - ward And point us to the skies. Its sto- ries all so might - y, Of men so
heav - en God's well- be- lov - ed Son, And how He bowed to sor- row, That we His
Bi - ble Thro' all life's fu- ture road; The watchword in life's bat - tle, The chart on

brave to see; The beau- ti - ful dear Bi - ble, Ii shall our teach-er be.
face might see,—The Bi - ble, O the Bi - ble, It shall our teach-er be.
life's dark sea,—The beau- ti - ful, dear Bi - ble, It shall our teach-er be. A-men.

Thy Word Have I Hid in My Heart. 62

(J.) C. AUSTIN MILES.

Thy Word have I hid in my heart, that I might not sin a - gainst Thee.

Bless - ed art Thou, O Lord;...... teach me Thy stat - utes. A - men.

63
Wonderful Words of Life.
P. P. B.
(J.)
Philip P. Bliss.
1. Sing them o - ver a - gain to me, Won-der- ful words of life, Let me
2. Christ, the bless-ed One, gives to all Won-der- ful words of life, List, O
3. Sweet - ly ech - o the gos - pel call Won-der- ful words of life, Of - fer
more of their beau-ty see, Won-der-ful words of life. Words of life and beau - ty,
list to His lov- ing call, Won-der-ful words of life. All so free-ly giv - en,
par-don and peace to all, Won-der-ful words of life. Je - sus, on - ly Sav- iour,
Teach me faith and du - ty;
Tell - ing us of heav - en,
Be our Guide for - ev - er,
Refrain.
Beau - ti - ful words, won-der - ful words, Won-der - ful
words of life, Beau- ti- ful words, won-der-ful words, Wonderful words of life.
64
Jesus, Thou Our Teacher Be.
Grace Gordon.
(P-J.)
Clyde Willard
1. Je - sus, Thou our Teach - er be, As we come to learn of Thee.
2. Teach us from the Word di - vine, May its ho - ly pa - ges shine,

Jesus, Thou Our Teacher Be.
Les-sons of Thy love im-part, May they live in ev-'ry heart!
May Thy light each spir-it fill, Teach us, Lord, to do Thy will! A-men.
Holy Bible, Word Divine.
65
C. AUSTIN MILES.
(J.)
Pleyel's Hymn.
1. Ho-ly Bi-ble, word di-vine I will make thy teach-ings mine,
2. Ho-ly Bi-ble, thou wilt be As a chart to show to me
3. Word of God I know thou art; Of my life be thou a part,
That my life may rich-er be By the wis-dom gain'd from Thee.
What is wrong and what is right, What is dark-ness, what is light.
Of my be-ing take con-trol, Not in part, but of the whole. A-men.
Copyright, MCMXXIX, by Hall-Mack Co. International Copyright Secured.
The Holy Word.
66
C. A. M.
(J.)
C. AUSTIN MILES.
1. How glo-rious is the Ho-ly Word That in my hand I hold;
2. I'll make its pre-cious teachings mine For wis-dom they shall give,
Its pre-cepts shine like per-fect gems In set-tings of fine gold.
And try to heed its warn-ing voice While here on earth I live.
Copyright, MCMXXIX, by Hall-Mack Co. International Copyright Secured.

67 The Song of the Book.

W. S. (J.) Rev. Wm. Stone.

1. Gen - e - sis and Ex - o - dus, Le - vit - i - cus and Numbers, With Deuter - on - o -
2. Job and Psalms and Pro - verbs and then Ec - cle - si - as - tes, With Song of Sol - o -
3. Ho - se - a and Joel, A - mos, O - be - di - ah, Jo - nah, Then Mi - cah, Na - hum,
4. Matthew. Mark and Luke and John, the writers of the Gos - pels, The Acts, the Book of
5. First and Second Thes - sa - lo - nians, First and Second Timothy, Then Ti - tus, Phi - le-
my com - plete the Books of law. Josh - ua, Judg - es, Ruth,
mon are Books of po - et - ry. I - sa - iah, Jer - e - mi - ah, Lam - en-
Hab - ak - kuk, with per - fect faith in God; Zeph - a - ni - ah,
His - t'ry Ro - mans fol - low next; First Cor - inthians, Sec - ond, then Gal-
mon and Hebrews, four - teen all. Sev'n E - pis - tles,
First and Sec - ond Sam - u - el, First Kings, Second Kings, Chroni - cles One and
ta - tions and E - ze - ki - el, Dan - iel fol - lows these might - y men of
Hag - ga - i, *"be strong and work," Zech - a - ri - ah, Mal - a - chi last of
a - tians and Eph - e - si - ans Tell us that we must *"gird on our arm - or"
James and Pet - er One and Two, John One, Two and Three, Jude, they were all with
Two; With Ez - ra, Esth - er, Ne - he - mi - ah are Books of his - to - ry.
God; All these are the Maj - or Prophets with mes - sage strong and clear.
all; And these are the Min - or Prophets and might - y men of God.
bright; Phil - ip - pians, Col - os - sians tell us *"we are complete" in Him.
Paul; And one book of Rev - e - la - tion, com - plete the Word of God.

* Key Phrase.

It's Just Like God the Father 68

C. R. F. (J.) CAROLYN R. FREEMAN.

1. Sum-mertime is knocking at the door, With her treasures fair, and her pleasures rare;
2. Bird notes trill a hap - py roun- de- lay, And they swee-tly fall, with such beauteous call,
3. Praise to God for love-ly blooming flow'rs; Lift your hearts and sing, let your voices ring,
Won - ders glad she's bring - ing as of yore; Joy is ev - 'ry - where.
Life is like a joy - ous mel - o - dy, Greet - ing one and all.
Thank Him for the gold - en sun - lit hours, And the joys they bring.
CHORUS.
It's just like God the Fa-ther, His bless-ings to be - stow; He wants us to be
hap - py, So He makes the blos-soms grow; He sends the smil-ing sunbeams From their
gold - en throne a - bove; It's just like God the Fa - ther, For God is Love.

69
An Evensong.
C. R. F.
(P.)
Carolyn R. Freeman.
1. When the eve - ning shad - ows gath - er, When I close my eyes in sleep,
2. In the morn - ing when I wak - en, Read - y for an - oth - er day,
3. In the dark, and in the day - light I will trust and have no fear,
I can know that God the Fa - ther Thro' the night will safe - ly keep.
God the Fa - ther will be with me, He will help me on my way.
I will pray to Him, be - liev - ing He my pray'r will sure - ly hear.
Chorus.
I will fear no ill, Through the long night still,
God has al - ways kept me, And I know He al - ways will.
Copyright, MCMXXIX, by Hall-Mack Co. International Copyright Secured.
70
The Father's Care.
Rebecca J. Weston.
(P.)
C. Austin Miles.
1. Fa - ther, we thank Thee for the night, And for the pleas - ant morn-ing light;
2. Help us to do the things we should, To be to oth - ers kind and good;
Copyright, MCMXXIX, by Hall-Mack Co. International Copyright Secured.

The Father's Care.

For rest and food and lov - ing care, And all that makes the day so fair.
In all we do in work or play, To grow more lov - ing ev - 'ry day. A-men.
When the Dawn is Breaking.
71
C. R. F.
(P.)
Carolyn R. Freeman.
1. When the dawn is break - ing, O'er the ro - sy sky,.........
2. Where the sun - beams play - ing Spread their gold - en cheer,......
3. Where the flow'rs are spring - ing And the grass - es grow,........
When the birds are wak - ing, In their nests on high.........
Where the breeze is stray - ing, God is al - ways near.........
Where sweet songs are ring - ing, And the brook - lets flow.........
Chorus.
Out where na-ture is glad and fair, Seek for God and you'll find Him there;
God the Fa-ther is ev - 'rywhere, And we're safe in His ten - der care.

72 For God So Loved the World.
John 3: 16.
(P–J.)
J. Lincoln Hall.
For God so loved the world...... that He gave His on - ly be -
For God................ so loved the world,
got - ten Son, that who - so - ev - er be - liev - eth in Him, who - so -
ev - er be - liev - eth in Him Should not per - ish, should not
per - ish, but have ev - er - last - ing life.................................
ev - er - last - ing life......
Copyright, MCMXX, by Hall-Mack Co. International Copyright Secured.
73 Father, Lead Me.
John Page Hopps.
(J.)
Louis M. Gottschalk.
1. Fa - ther, lead me day by day, Ev - er in Thy right - eous way;
2. When in dan - ger make me brave, Make me know that Thou canst save;
3. When I'm tempted to do wrong, Make me stead - fast, wise and strong;

Father, Lead Me.
Teach me to be pure and true, Show me what I ought to do.
Keep me ev - er by Thy side, Let me in Thy love a - bide
And when all a - lone I stand, Shield me with Thy might-y hand. A - men.
God is Near.
74
Mattie B. Shannon.
(P.)
Grace L. Hosmer.
Grazioso.
1. When the darkness lies O'er the shadowed skies, And we rest in slum-ber deep,
2. When the morning bright Fills the sky with light, Still His love is ver - y near,
There's a Fa-ther's love Watching from a - bove, And He guards us while we sleep.
As we work or play Thro' each hap-py day, There is naught that we need fear.
Chorus.
God is near, God is near, With a ten - der, lov - ing care;
God is near, God is near, And He safe - ly keeps us ev - ry-where.

75
For Us, His Children.
G. L. S.
(P–J.)
Grace L. Hosmer.
1. The love of God for us is ev - 'ry - where. His smile is in the golden sunlight fair; His voice is in the gen - tly stir-ring air, For we are His be - lov - ed chil - dren.
2. The won - der of the sky so blue, so deep, The won - der of the stars that guard our sleep. The hap - py lit - tle dreams that o'er us creep, He gives them un - to us, His chil - dren.
3. So per - fect is the work done by His hand; Each ti - ny feath - ered bird by Him was plann'd. With love - ly pictures He has fill'd the land, And all for His be - lov - ed chil - dren.
Refrain.
Be - cause He loves us so, Be - cause He loves us so. For us the earth with all its joy, Be - cause He loves us so.
rit.
Copyright, MCMXXIX, by Hall-Mack Co. International Copyright Secured.
76
He'll Not Forget His Little Ones.
Anonymous.
(B.)
Joseph Barnby.
God made the birds and flow'rs, And all things large and small; He'll

He'll Not Forget His Little Ones.

not for - get His lit - tle ones; I know He loves them all. A - men.
God is Love
77
ELSIE DUNCAN YALE
(P-J.)
L. VON BEETHOVEN
SOP. AND ALTO
Arr. by ALFRED JUDSON
1. Have you heard the whis-per of the breeze? "God is love, God is love!"
2. Have you heard the birds' ex-ult - ant notes? "God is love, God is love!"
3. Have you heard the sing-ing of the sea? "God is love, God is love!"
Have you heard the murm'ring of the trees, Sing-ing soft - ly, sweetly, "God is love?"
Down from distant heights the car - ol floats, Ring-ing glad-ly, clear-ly, "God is love!"
Where the crest - ed bil - lows toss so free, Tell-ing, tell - ing ev - er, "God is love!"
CHORUS
Bless - ed song, ech - o on, Glad mes - sage sound for - ev - er; Ring - ing
rit.
'neath the ra - diant skies a - bove, God is love, God is love!

78
We'll Follow Christ.
MATTIE B. SHANNON.
(J.)
GRACE L. HOSMER.
1. All our life is like an er - rand true, That our God has giv - en us to do, And to keep our mis - sion pure and right, We must live as in the Father's sight.
2. There's a pat - tern wait - ing large and small, For the Fa - ther sent His Son to all, As He lived for oth - ers day by day, We must try to fol - low in His way.
3. O the tasks are ma - ny for our hands, As we meet the call of life's de - mands, There's a place no oth - er soul may fill, As we strive to do the Father's will.
CHORUS.
We'll fol - low, we'll fol - low, Follow Christ who taught the way; O glad - ly we'll fol - low, Un - to Je - sus looking ev -'ry day.
Copyright, MCMXXIX, by Hall-Mack Co. International Copyright Secured.
79
Jesus Thinks of Me.
MATTIE B. SHANNON.
(J.)
ARTHUR WILTON.
1. There's a song my heart is sing - ing, O so joy - ous - ly!
2. There's a song my heart is sing - ing, Giv'n, dear Lord, by Thee,
Copyright, MCMXXIX, by Hall-Mack Co. International Copyright Secured.

Jesus Thinks of Me.
Day by day 'tis glad - ness bring - ing, Je - sus thinks of me!
O'er and o'er 'tis sweet - ly ring - ing, Je - sus thinks of me!
In the Temple.
80
Flora Kirkland.
(J.)
Howard E. Smith.
1. In the tem - ple, in the tem - ple Stood a lit - tle boy one day,
2. It was Je - sus who was teach - ing And they lis - tened to His word,
3. With the teachers there they found Him, Tho' a low - ly, learn - ing youth,
4. "Let us ev - er then be loy - al To our God, and church, and home,"
And the doc - tors wondered great - ly At the words they heard Him say.
As He told them of His mis - sion From the great and might - y Lord.
But His an - swers as He told them Were complete with Bi - ble truth.
Ev - er faith - ful, ev - er trust - ing, "Nev - er mind - ing what may come."
Chorus.
It was Je - sus! It was Je - sus! He was but a lit - tle child,
rit.
But the light of heav'n was shin - ing In His face so pure and mild.

81 Follow Me.
ELSIE DUNCAN YALE.
(J.)
ALICE LARRY WOODCOCK.
QUESTION.
1. Who are these be - side the sea, Mend - ing nets so bus - i - ly?
2. Who are these who hear the call, Let their nets half-mend - ed fall?
3. Can we hear His voice to - day, Call - ing to His ho - ly way?
ANSWER.
These are low - ly fish - ers toil - ing, Fish - er-men of Gal - i - lee.
These are fish - ers glad - ly hear - ing, Glad - ly they are leav - ing all!
Yes, the Mas - ter still in - vites us, Haste, His gen - tle word o - bey.
ALL.
Lift your eyes, O fish - ers low - ly! Lo, there comes the Christ so ho - ly,
Fish - ers true, His name con - fess - ing, He will give you great - est bless - ing,
Still the lov - ing Lord is speak - ing, For His help - ers He is seek - ing,
'Tis the Mas - ter who has called you, "Fol - low, fol - low Me!"......
For the Son of God has called you, "Fol - low, fol - low Me!"......
'Tis the Mas - ter who is call - ing, "Fol - low, fol - low Me!"......
Copyright, MCMXXIX, by Hall-Mack Co. International Copyright Secured.
82 Jesus, Friend of Little Children.
Rev. WALTER J. MATHAMS.
(B–P.)
J. H. MAUNDER.
1. Je - sus, Friend of lit - tle chil - dren, Be a Friend to me,
2. Teach me how to grow in good - ness Dai - ly as I grow;

Jesus, Friend of Little Children.

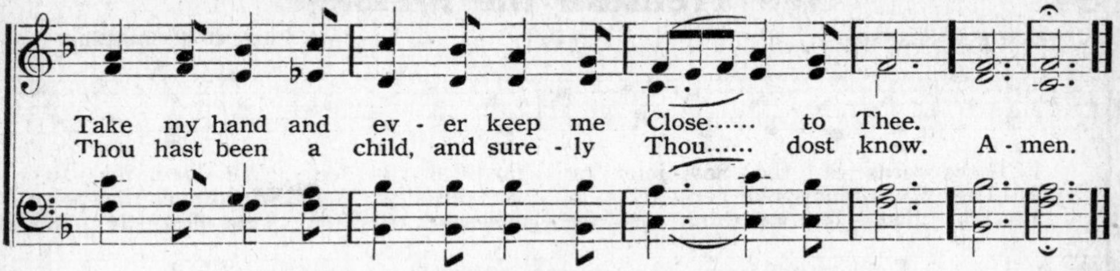

Take my hand and ever keep me Close...... to Thee.
Thou hast been a child, and surely Thou...... dost know. A-men.

O Master-Workman of the Race. 83

JAY T. STOCKING. (P-J.) SAMUEL A. WARD.

1. O Master-workman of the race, Thou Man of Galilee,........
Who with the eyes of early youth Eternal things did see,........
We thank Thee for Thy boyhood faith That shone Thy whole life through;
"Did ye not know it is My work My Father's work to do?"

2. O Carpenter of Nazareth, Builder of life divine,......
Who shapest man to God's own law, Thyself the fair design.......
Build us a tow'r of Christ-like height, That we the land may view,......
And see like Thee our noblest work Our Father's work to do.

3. O Thou who didst the vision send And gives to each his task,......
And with the task sufficient strength, Show us Thy will, we ask;......
Give us a conscience bold and good, Give us a purpose true,......
That it may be our highest joy, Our Father's work to do. A-men.

84 We Treasure the Message.

MATTIE B. SHANNON. (P.) CAROLYN R. FREEMAN.

1. These words of the Sav - iour by far Gal - i - lee We love, for to us they are giv - en; "O suf - fer the chil - dren to come un - to Me, Of such is the king - dom of heav - en."
2. The Sav - iour spoke gen - tly in ac - cents so low, With hands that were outstretched in bless - ing, And just like the chil - dren of days long a - go, We too are His mes - sage pos - sess - ing.
3. So, glad - ly we think of the mes - sage so free, That clear - ly and sweet - ly is ring - ing; As swift - ly we an - swer His "Come un - to Me," A trib - ute of love we are bring - ing.
CHORUS.
"O suf - fer the children," blest words of the Sav - iour, Sounding so sweet - ly long a - ges thro'; With voic - es now ring - ing our thanks we are sing - ing, We treas - ure the mes - sage so true.

In Christ There Is No East or West. 85

JOHN OXENHAM. (J.) ALEXANDER R. REINAGLE.

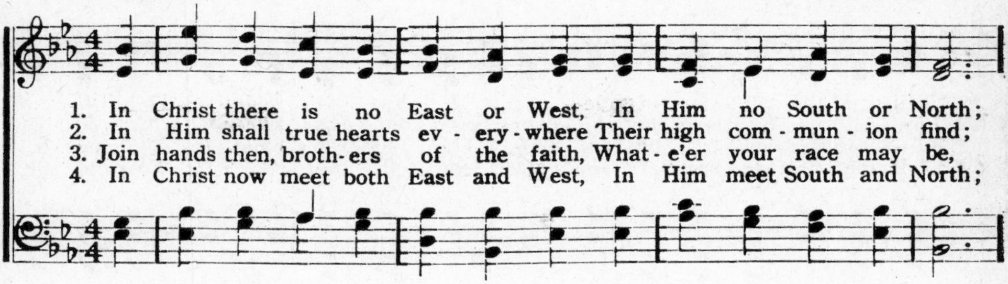

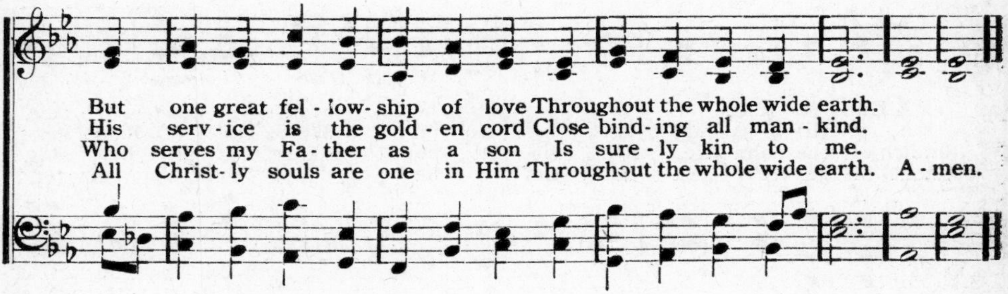

1. In Christ there is no East or West, In Him no South or North; But one great fel - low- ship of love Throughout the whole wide earth.
2. In Him shall true hearts ev - ery - where Their high com - mun - ion find; His serv - ice is the gold - en cord Close bind - ing all man - kind.
3. Join hands then, broth - ers of the faith, What - e'er your race may be, Who serves my Fa - ther as a son Is sure - ly kin to me.
4. In Christ now meet both East and West, In Him meet South and North; All Christ - ly souls are one in Him Throughout the whole wide earth. A - men.

In Our Work and in Our Play. 86

(J.) Arr. from a Mediæval French Melody by RICHARD REDHEAD.

W. CHATTERTON DIX.

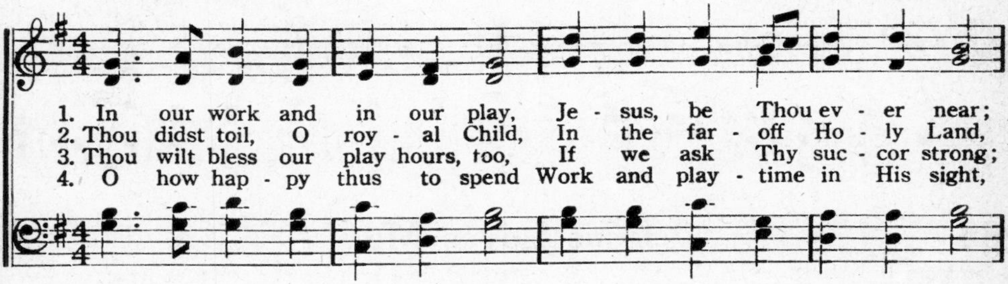

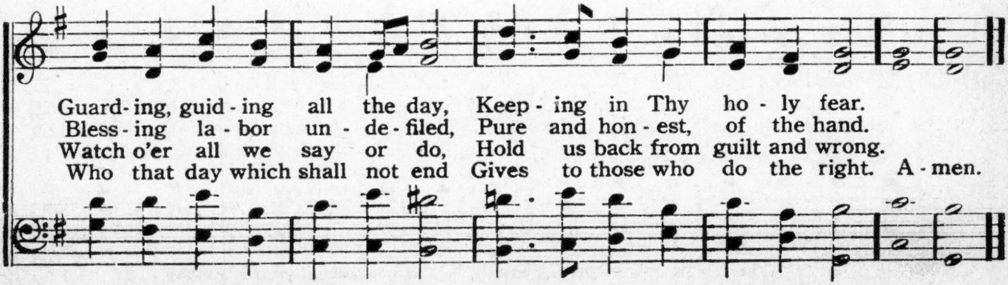

1. In our work and in our play, Je - sus, be Thou ev - er near; Guard - ing, guid - ing all the day, Keep - ing in Thy ho - ly fear.
2. Thou didst toil, O roy - al Child, In the far - off Ho - ly Land, Bless - ing la - bor un - de - filed, Pure and hon - est, of the hand.
3. Thou wilt bless our play hours, too, If we ask Thy suc - cor strong; Watch o'er all we say or do, Hold us back from guilt and wrong.
4. O how hap - py thus to spend Work and play - time in His sight, Who that day which shall not end Gives to those who do the right. A - men.

87 Tell Me the Stories of Jesus.
W. H. PARKER.
(P-J.)
F. A. CHALLINOR.
1. Tell me the sto-ries of Je-sus I love to hear; Things I would ask Him to tell me If He were here; Scenes by the way-side, Tales of the sea, Sto-ries of Je-sus, Tell them to me.
2. First let me hear how the chil-dren Stood round His knee; And I shall fan-cy His bless-ing Rest-ing on me; Words full of kind-ness, Deeds full of grace All in the love-light Of Je-sus' face,
3. In-to the cit-y I'd fol-low, The chil-dren's band, Wav-ing a branch of the palm-tree High in my hand; One of His her-alds, Yes, I would sing Loud-est ho-san-nas! Je-sus is King.
4. Tell me in ac-cents of won-der, How rolled the sea, Toss-ing the boat in a tem-pest On Gal-i-lee! And how the Mas-ter, Read-y and kind, Chid-ed the bil-lows, And hushed the wind.
rall.
88 Jesus Loves Me.
ANNA L. WARNER.
(P. Chorus B.)
WM. B. BRADBURY.
1. Je-sus loves me! This I know, For the Bi-ble tells me so; Lit-tle
2. Je-sus loves me! He who died, Heav-en's gate to o-pen wide; He will
3. Je-sus loves me! Loves me still, Tho' I'm ver-y weak and ill; From His
4. Je-sus loves me! He will stay Close be-side me all the way; If I

Jesus Loves Me.

CHORUS.
ones to Him be-long; They are weak, but He is strong.
wash a-way my sin, Let His lit-tle child come in.
shin-ing throng on high, Comes to watch me where I lie.
love Him when I die, He will take me home on high.
Yes, Je-sus loves me!
Yes, Je-sus loves me! Yes, Je-sus loves me! The Bi-ble tells me so.
Jesus Bids Us Shine.
89
EMILY HUNTINGTON MILLER.
(B.)
1. Je-sus bids us shine With a clear, pure light, Like a lit-tle
2. Je-sus bids us shine First of all for Him; Well He sees and
can-dle Burn-ing in the night; In the world is dark-ness,
knows it If our light grows dim. He looks down from heav-en
So we must shine, You in your small cor-ner, And I in mine.
To see us shine. You in your small cor-ner, And I in mine.

90
'Tis Not Far to Jesus.
FANNY J. CROSBY.
(P–J.)
W. H. DOANE.
1. 'Tis not far to Je - sus, He is ev - 'ry - where, Watch-ing o'er His chil - dren With a ten - der care.
2. 'Tis not far to Je - sus, No, 'tis ver - y near; He is all a - round us, He is with us here.
3. If we want to love Him Let us go and pray; Then our hearts can find Him, Now, this ver - y day.
CHORUS.
Ear - ly if we seek Him, Ear - ly we shall find Him; 'Tis not far to Je - sus, He is ev - 'ry - where.
Copyright, MDCCCLXXX, by Biglow & Main Co. Hope Pub. Co., owner. Used by per.
91
Jesus Calls Me.
A. A. P.
(P.)
A. A. PAYN.
1. Sweet is the voice of a moth - er Call - ing so ten - der - ly,.......... Sweet - er the voice of the Sav - iour, Say - ing, "O come to Me."
2. Fair are the flow - ers that blos - som Out in the mead - ow free,......... Fair - er the face of my Sav - iour When He is call - ing me.
3. Glad - ly to Him I am com - ing, All un - to Him I give,......... Will - ing - ly walk in His foot - steps, Serv - ing Him while I live.
Copyright, MCMXIV, by Hall-Mack Co. International Copyright Secured.

Jesus Calls Me.

CHORUS.

I am so glad that He loves me, Je-sus loves me, Je - sus loves me;
I am so glad that He calls me, For-ev-er His child to be.......

I Think When I Read That Sweet Story. 92

JEMIMA LUKE. (P.) Traditional English Melody.

1. I think when I read that sweet sto - ry of old When
Je - sus was here a - mong men, How He called lit - tle chil - dren as
lambs to His fold, I should like to have been with them then.

2. I wish that His hands had been placed on my head, That His
arms had been thrown a - round me, And that I might have seen His kind
look when He said, "Let the lit - tle ones come un - to Me."

3. Yet still to His foot-stool in pray'r I may go, And
ask for a share in His love; And if I now earn - est - ly
seek Him be - low, I shall see Him and hear Him a - bove.

93 No Child is Too Little.
C. R. F.
(P.)
CAROLYN R. FREEMAN.
1. No child is too lit - tle for Je - sus, He loves and He cares for them all,
2. No child is too lit - tle to serve Him, There al- ways is something to do;
The Mas- ter is wait- ing to bless them, No mat- ter how young or how small.
And if we make someone else hap - py, Then we will be hap- pi - er, too.
CHORUS.
No child is too lit - tle to love Him, And learn of His heav- en - ly throne,
For Je - sus love all lit - tle chil - dren, And wants ev -'ry child for His own.
Copyright, MCMXXIX, by Hall-Mack Co. International Copyright Secured.
94 O Christ, the Way, the Truth, the Life.
GEORGE L. SQUIER.
(J.)
JOHN BACCHUS DYKES.
1. O Christ, the Way, the Truth, the Life, Show me the liv - ing way,
2. Teach me Thy truth, O Christ, my Light, The truth that makes me free,
3. The life that Thou a - lone canst give, Im - part in love to me,

O Christ, the Way, the Truth, the Life.

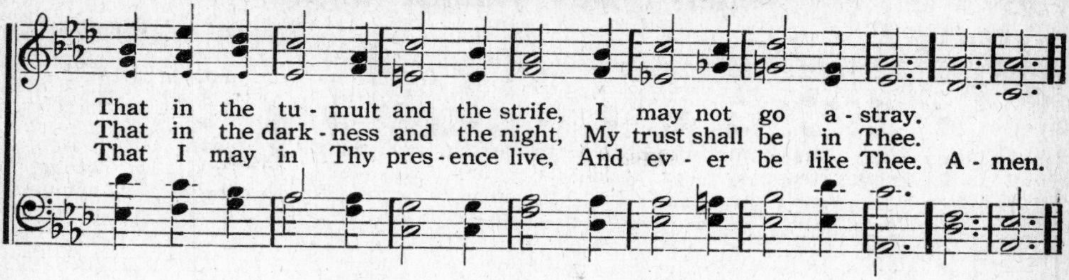

That in the tu - mult and the strife, I may not go a - stray.
That in the dark - ness and the night, My trust shall be in Thee.
That I may in Thy pres - ence live, And ev - er be like Thee. A - men.

We Belong to Jesus. 95

(J.)

MATTIE B. SHANNON. HALDOR LILLENAS.

1. We have heard the Sav - iour's voice, Say - ing, "Fol - low Me,"
We glad - ly come like those of old, Be - side fair Gal - i - lee.

2. May the name of Christ our King, Nev - er be de - nied;
His cross up - lift - ed as our sign, We'll serve the Cru - ci - fied.

3. Not with sound of stir - ring drums, Serve with hosts of youth.
We'll win the world with kind - ly deeds, And lov - ing words of truth.

CHORUS.

We be - long to Je - sus And we'll do His will,
Will - ing to go an - y - where for we know That He guides us still.

96
When Jesus Was a Child.
(J.)
C. R. F.
CAROLYN R. FREEMAN.
1. When Je - sus came from heav'n to earth, So man - y years a - go,
2. I know He nev - er told a lie, He nev - er did a wrong,
3. When Je - sus was a lit - tle boy, He liked to laugh and play,
Like ev - 'ry oth - er boy He had To live, and learn, and grow.
His moth - er could de - pend on Him Thro' all the whole day long.
As well as an - y oth - er lad Who lived in Je - sus' day.
CHORUS.
He had His dai - ly les - sons, And help - ful tasks to do,
For Je - sus was a *faith - ful child We can be *faith - ful, too.
Copyright, MCMXXIX, by Hall-Mack Co International Copyright Secured.
* Second Chorus use "Truthful," third Chorus "Loving."
97
Jesus, Loving Jesus.
(B-P.)
C. A. M.
C. AUSTIN MILES.
1. Who will hear us when we pray, And will teach us what to say?
2. Who will help us to do right And will make our lives more bright,
Copyright, MCMXXIX, by Hall-Mack Co. International Copyright Secured.

Jesus, Loving Jesus.
Who will bless us ev - 'ry day? Je - sus, lov - ing Je - sus.
Lov - ing us by day and night? Je - sus, lov - ing Je - sus. A - men.
I've Found a Friend.
98
J. G. Small.
(J.)
Geo. C. Stebbins.
1. I've found a Friend, O such a Friend! He lov'd me ere I knew Him;
2. I've found a Friend, O such a Friend! He bled, He died to save me;
3. I've found a Friend, O such a Friend! All pow'r to Him is giv - en,
4. I've found a Friend, O such a Friend! So kind, and true, and ten - der,
He drew me with the cords of love, And thus He bound me to Him.
And not a - lone the gift of life. But His own self He gave me.
To guard me on my on - ward course, And bring me save to heav - en.
So wise a Coun - sel - lor and Guide, So might - y a De - fend - er!
And 'round my heart still close - ly twine Those ties which naught can sev - er,
Nought that I have my own I call. I hold it for the Giv - er:
Th' e - ter - nal glo - ries gleam a - far, To nerve my faint en - deav - or:
From Him, who loves me now, so well, What pow'r my soul can sev - er?
For I am His, and He is mine, For - ev - er and for - ev - er.
My heart, my strength, my life, my all, Are His, and His for - ev - er.
So now to watch, to work, to war, And then to rest for - ev - er.
Shall life or death, or earth or hell? No; I am His for - ev - er.

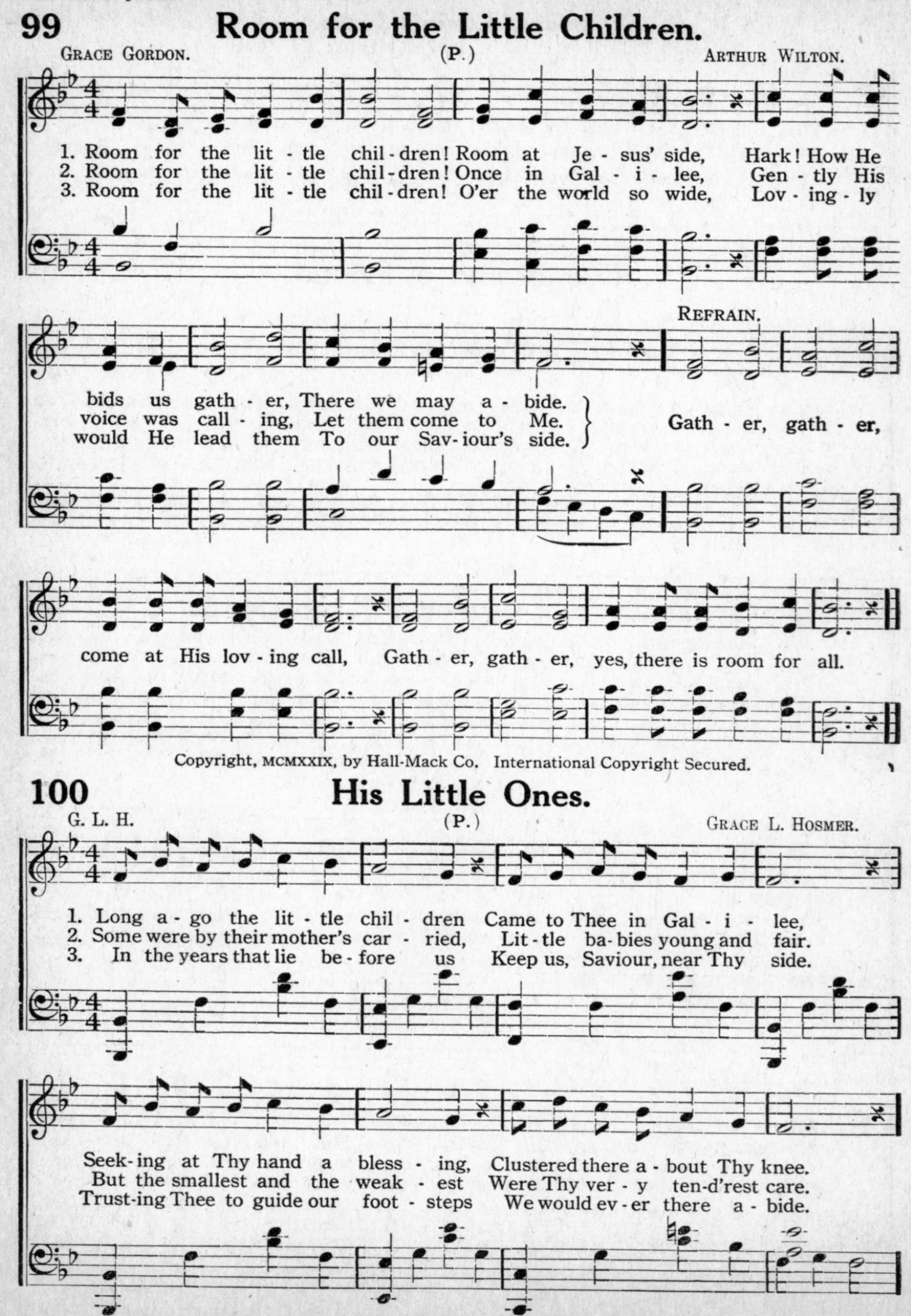
99
Room for the Little Children.
GRACE GORDON.
(P.)
ARTHUR WILTON.
1. Room for the lit - tle chil - dren! Room at Je - sus' side, Hark! How He bids us gath - er, There we may a - bide.
2. Room for the lit - tle chil - dren! Once in Gal - i - lee, Gen - tly His voice was call - ing, Let them come to Me.
3. Room for the lit - tle chil - dren! O'er the world so wide, Lov - ing - ly would He lead them To our Sav - iour's side.
REFRAIN.
Gath - er, gath - er, come at His lov - ing call, Gath - er, gath - er, yes, there is room for all.
Copyright, MCMXXIX, by Hall-Mack Co. International Copyright Secured.
100
His Little Ones.
G. L. H.
(P.)
GRACE L. HOSMER.
1. Long a - go the lit - tle chil - dren Came to Thee in Gal - i - lee, Seek - ing at Thy hand a bless - ing, Clustered there a - bout Thy knee.
2. Some were by their mother's car - ried, Lit - tle ba - bies young and fair. But the smallest and the weak - est Were Thy ver - y ten - d'rest care.
3. In the years that lie be - fore us Keep us, Saviour, near Thy side. Trust - ing Thee to guide our foot - steps We would ev - er there a - bide.
Copyright, MCMXXIX, by Hall-Mack Co. International Copyright Secured.

His Little Ones.

CHORUS.
Let Thy blessings then de-scend On Thy chil-dren as they pray.
May love reign with-in our hearts On this joy-ful Sab - bath day.
Jesus, the Same!
101
ELSIE DUNCAN YALE.
(P.)
ARTHUR WILTON.
1. He Who bless'd the chil - dren, in the days of old, Still will bid them wel - come, to His shel - t'ring fold!
2. He Who called the fish - ers, by the sun - lit sea, Still is gen - tly call - ing, "Fol - low, fol - low me!"
3. He Who taught dis - ci - ples on a sun - lit hill, Brings a heav'n-ly mes - sage, to His chil - dren still!
4. He Who walked of old - en paths of Gal - i - lee, All un-seen is near us, Friend and Guide to be!
REFRAIN.
Sing of Christ our Sav - iour, ev - er-more the same, May we seek to serve Him, Bless His ho - ly name!

102 Let the Words of My Mouth.

(J.) C. AUSTIN MILES.

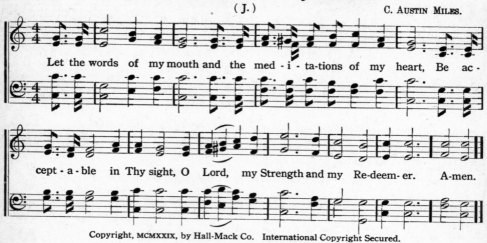

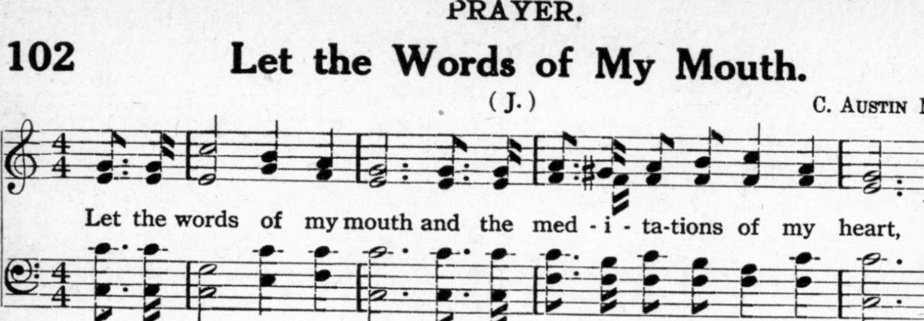
Let the words of my mouth and the med - i - ta-tions of my heart, Be ac -

cept - a - ble in Thy sight, O Lord, my Strength and my Re-deem- er. A-men.

103 He Prayeth Best Who Loveth Best.

(J.) CLYDE WILLARD.

He pray - eth best, who lov - eth best all things both great and small;
For the dear God who lov - est us, He made and lov - eth all.

104 Enter Into His Gates.

(P–J.) C. AUSTIN MILES.

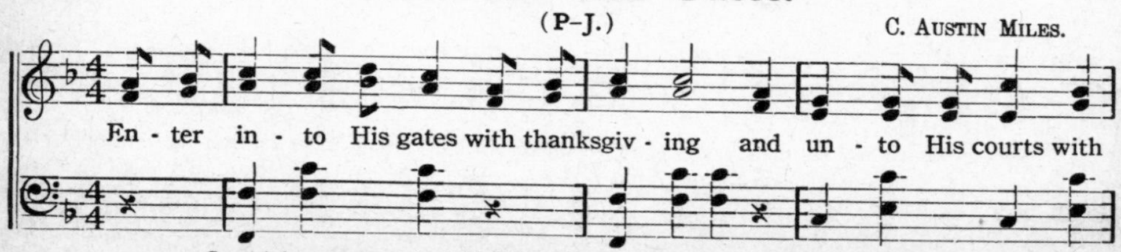
En - ter in - to His gates with thanksgiv - ing and un - to His courts with

Enter Into His Gates

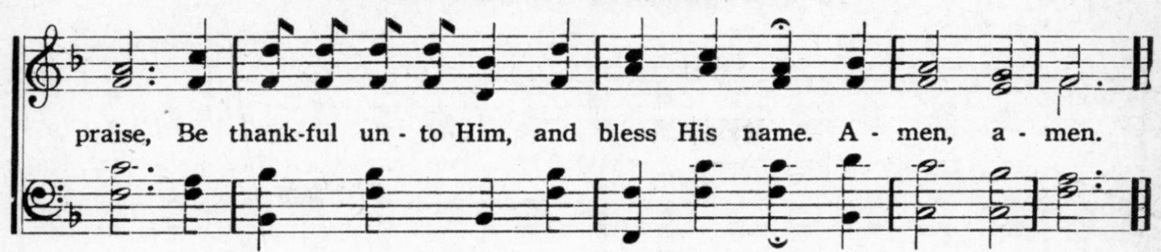
praise, Be thank-ful un - to Him, and bless His name. A - men, a - men.

O Father, Hear My Morning Prayer. 105

F. A. Percy. (J.) Arthur Cottman.

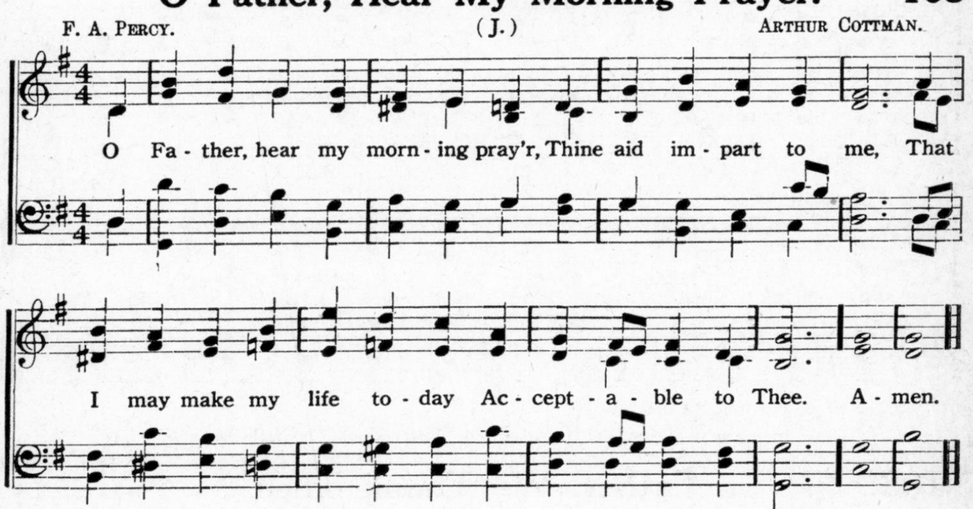
O Fa - ther, hear my morn - ing pray'r, Thine aid im - part to me, That
I may make my life to - day Ac - cept - a - ble to Thee. A - men.

To Think and Do Right. 106

Mabel E. Locker. (P–J.) C. Austin Miles.

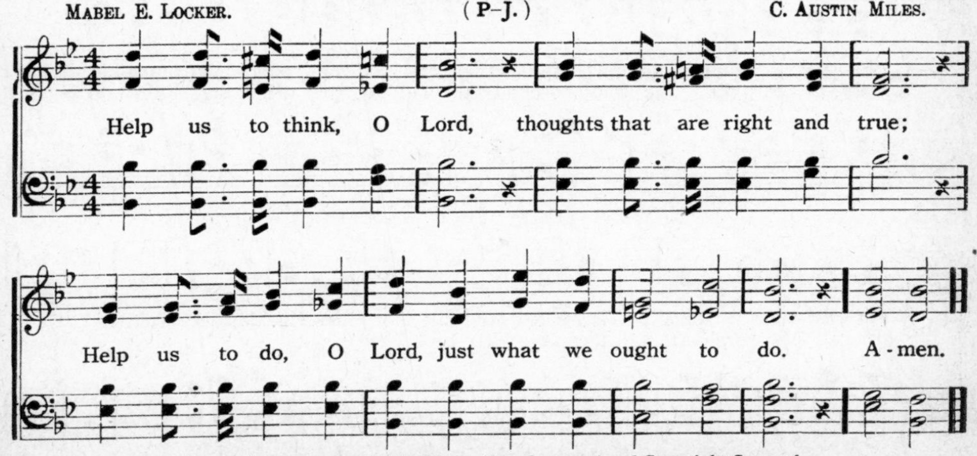
Help us to think, O Lord, thoughts that are right and true;
Help us to do, O Lord, just what we ought to do. A - men.

107 Hymn of Thanks.

C. F. O. (B.) ALFRED JUDSON.

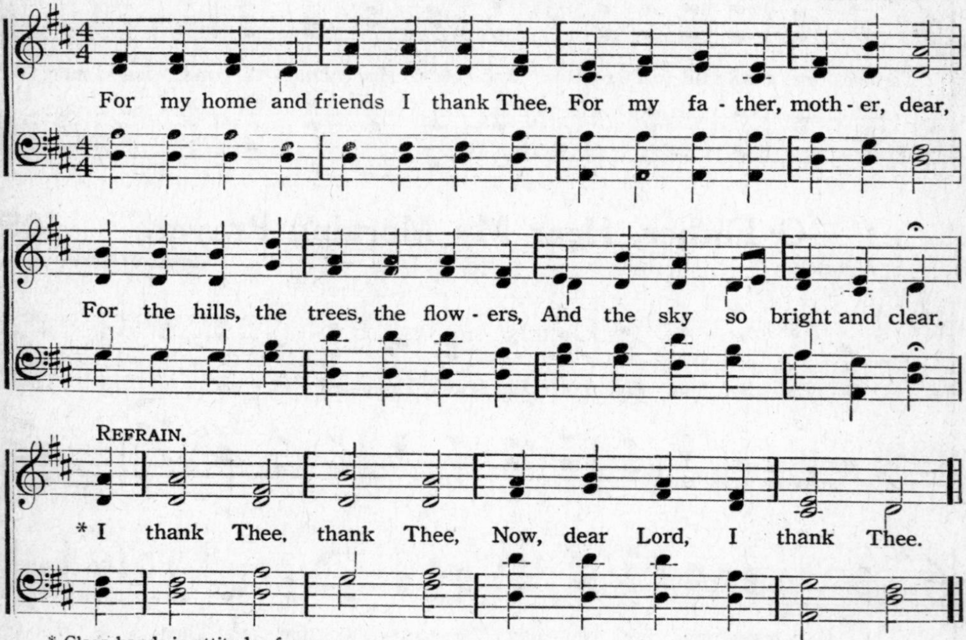

For my home and friends I thank Thee, For my fa - ther, moth - er, dear,
For the hills, the trees, the flow - ers, And the sky so bright and clear.

REFRAIN.

* I thank Thee, thank Thee, Now, dear Lord, I thank Thee.

* Clasp hands in attitude of prayer.

108 Father, We Thank Thee.

REBECCA J. WESTON. (B–P.) PETER RITTER. Arr. by WILLIAM H. MONK.

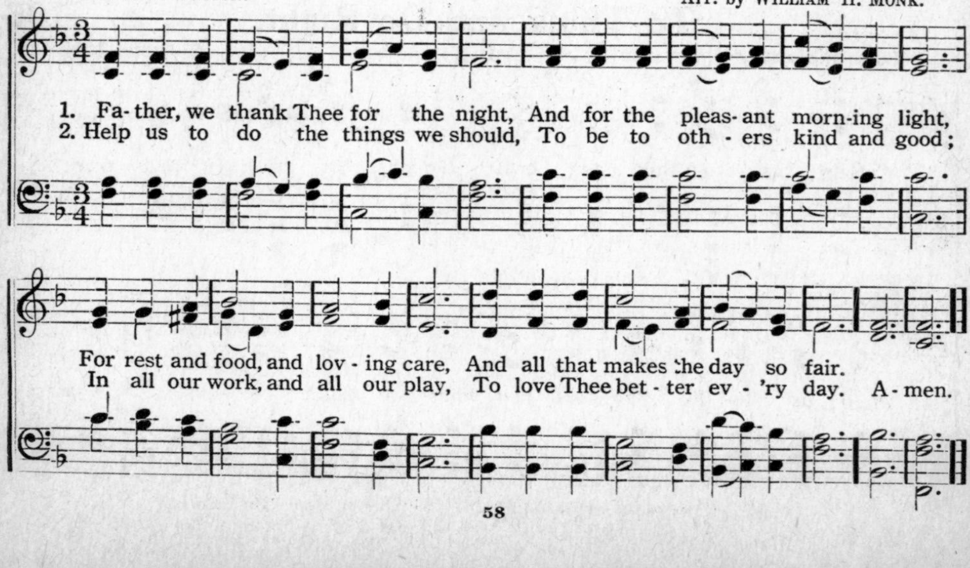

1. Fa-ther, we thank Thee for the night, And for the pleas-ant morn-ing light,
For rest and food, and lov - ing care, And all that makes the day so fair.

2. Help us to do the things we should, To be to oth - ers kind and good;
In all our work, and all our play, To love Thee bet - ter ev - 'ry day. A-men.

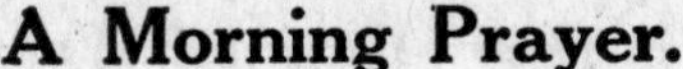

A Morning Prayer. 109

ALICE WHITSON NORTON. (P-J.) MAY F. LAWRENCE.

Moderato.

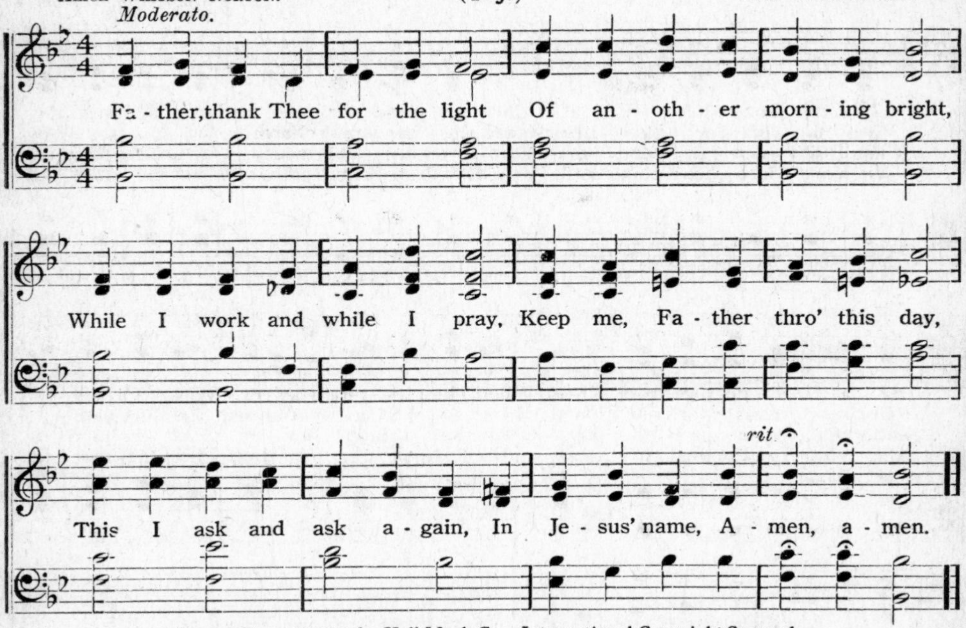

Fa - ther, thank Thee for the light Of an - oth - er morn - ing bright,
While I work and while I pray, Keep me, Fa - ther thro' this day,
This I ask and ask a - gain, In Je - sus' name, A - men, a - men.

rit.

Saviour, Teach Me Day by Day. 110

JANE E. LEESON. (J.) CARL M. VON WEBER.

1. Sav - iour, teach me day by day, Love's sweet les - son to o - bey:
Sweet - er les - son can - not be— Lov - ing Him who first loved me.
2. With a child - like heart of love, At Thy bid - ding may I move;
Prompt to serve and fol - low Thee— Lov - ing Him who first loved me.
3. Teach me all Thy steps to trace, Strong to fol - low in Thy grace;
Learn - ing how to love from Thee— Lov - ing Him who first loved me.
4. Love in lov - ing finds em - ploy, In o - be - dience all her joy;
Ev - er new that joy will be— Lov - ing Him who first loved me. A - men.

In the Hour of Trial.

JAMES MONTGOMERY. (J.) SPENCER LANE.

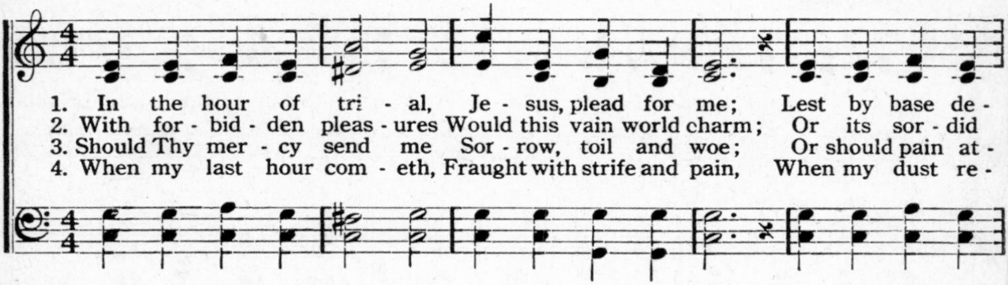

1. In the hour of tri - al, Je - sus, plead for me; Lest by base de -
2. With for - bid - den pleas - ures Would this vain world charm; Or its sor - did
3. Should Thy mer - cy send me Sor - row, toil and woe; Or should pain at -
4. When my last hour com - eth, Fraught with strife and pain, When my dust re -

ni - al I de - part from Thee. When Thou see'st me wav - er, With a look re -
treas - ures Spread to work me harm; Bring to my re - mem - brance Sad Geth - sem - a -
tend me On my path be - low; Grant that I may nev - er Fail Thy hand to
turn - eth To the dust a - gain; On Thy truth re - ly - ing, Thro' that mor - tal

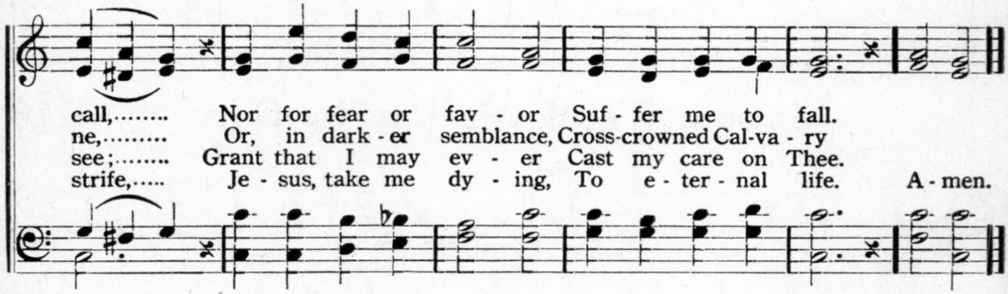

call,........ Nor for fear or fav - or Suf - fer me to fall.
ne,......... Or, in dark - er semblance, Cross-crowned Cal - va - ry
see;........ Grant that I may ev - er Cast my care on Thee.
strife,..... Je - sus, take me dy - ing, To e - ter - nal life. A - men.

112 Lord, Who Lovest Little Children.

(B.) Adapted from VINCENT NOVELLO.

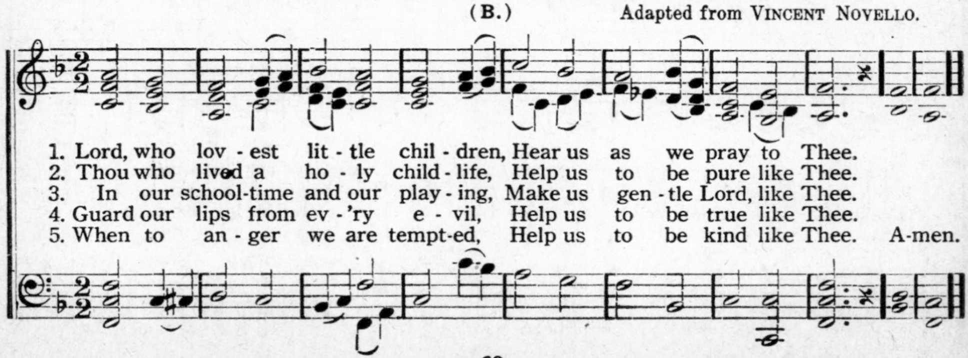

1. Lord, who lov - est lit - tle chil - dren, Hear us as we pray to Thee.
2. Thou who lived a ho - ly child - life, Help us to be pure like Thee.
3. In our school-time and our play - ing, Make us gen - tle Lord, like Thee.
4. Guard our lips from ev - 'ry e - vil, Help us to be true like Thee.
5. When to an - ger we are tempt - ed, Help us to be kind like Thee. A-men.

Father, Lead Me Day by Day. 113

(J.)

JOHN P. HOPPS. MAY F. LAWRENCE.

1. Father, lead me day by day, Ever in Thine own sweet way;
Teach me to be pure and true; Show me what I ought to do.

2. When in danger, make me brave, Make me know that Thou canst save;
Keep me safe by Thy dear side; Let me in Thy love abide.

3. When I'm tempted to do wrong, Make me steadfast, wise, and strong;
And when all alone I stand, Shield me with Thy mighty hand.

REFRAIN.

Father, hear this pray'r I make, This I ask for Jesus' sake. Amen.

The Golden Key. 114

(P.)

JOHN PARKER. JNO. R. SWENEY.

1. Prayer is the key For the bending knee To open the morn's first hours,
See the incense rise To the starry skies, Like perfume from the flow'rs.
2. Not a soul so sad, Nor a heart so glad, When cometh the shades of night,
But the daybreak song Will the joy prolong, And darkness turn to light. Amen.

115 We Are Building.

MATTIE B. SHANNON. (J.) GRACE L. HOSMER.

1. In the bright-ness of the morn we are build - ing, As our
2. We are care - ful of the way we are work - ing, Lest an
youth - ful hours so swift - ly pass a - way; 'Tis our char - ac - ters we
er - ror in our build - ing we should see, As a tem - ple is the
ev - er are mak - ing, With the help of our God day by day.
life - work we're rear - ing, That will stand thro' the storms yet to be.
REFRAIN.
Strong and true as the days go by, Hour by hour for the right we'll
try; O we're building, dai - ly build - ing For the life on high!

O What can Little Hands Do? 116

(P.)

J. S. Witty.

1. O what can lit-tle hands do To please the King of heav'n? The lit-tle hands some work may try That will some sim-ple want sup-ply: Such grace to mine be giv'n.
2. O what can lit-tle lips do To please the King of heav'n? The lit-tle lips can praise and pray, And gen-tle words of kind-ness say: Such grace to mine be giv'n.
3. O what can lit-tle eyes do To please the King of heav'n? The lit-tle eyes can upward look, Can learn to read God's ho-ly Book: Such grace to mine be giv'n.
4. O what can lit-tle hearts do To please the King of heav'n? Young hearts, if He His Spir-it send, Can love their Maker, Saviour, Friend: Such grace to mine be giv'n.

To Thy Father and Thy Mother. 117

A. R. Cousin.

(P.)

Arr. from "Psalmodia Sacra," Gotha.

1. To thy fa-ther and thy moth-er Hon-or, love, and rev-'rence pay; This command, be-fore all oth-er, Must a Chris-tian child o-bey.
2. Je-sus Christ, my Lord, ful-filled it, In His home at Naz-a-reth— So His heav'nly Fa-ther will'd it— While a child He dwelt be-neath.
3. Help me, Lord, in this sweet du-ty; Guide me in Thy steps di-vine; Show me all the joy and beau-ty Of o-be-dience such as Thine. A-men.

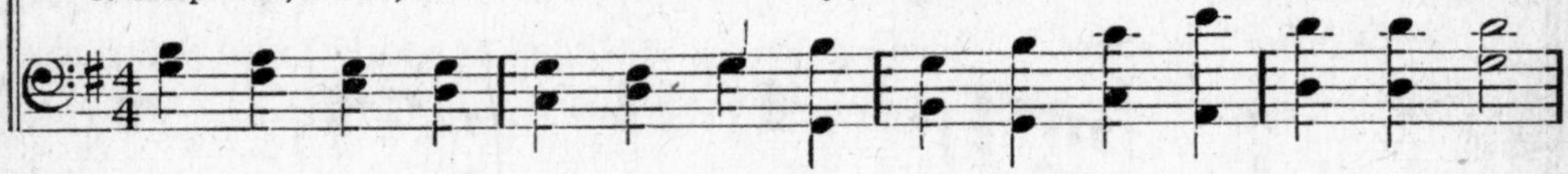

118 I Would Be a Little Sunbeam.

MIRIAM E. ARNOLD. (P.) CHAS. H. GABRIEL.

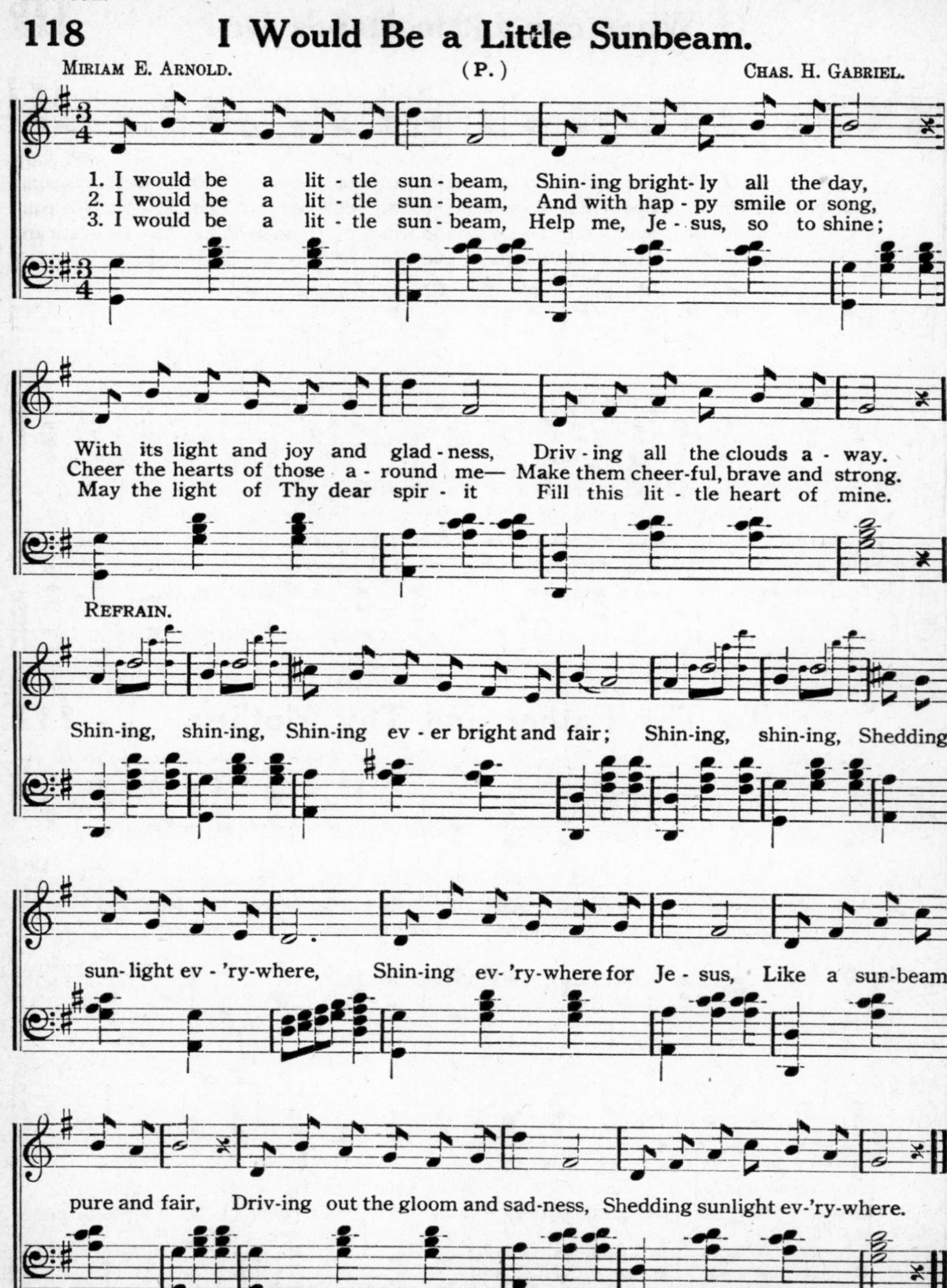
1. I would be a lit - tle sun - beam, Shin - ing bright - ly all the day,
2. I would be a lit - tle sun - beam, And with hap - py smile or song,
3. I would be a lit - tle sun - beam, Help me, Je - sus, so to shine;
With its light and joy and glad - ness, Driv - ing all the clouds a - way.
Cheer the hearts of those a - round me— Make them cheer - ful, brave and strong.
May the light of Thy dear spir - it Fill this lit - tle heart of mine.
REFRAIN.
Shin - ing, shin - ing, Shin - ing ev - er bright and fair; Shin - ing, shin - ing, Shedding
sun - light ev - 'ry - where, Shin - ing ev - 'ry - where for Je - sus, Like a sun - beam
pure and fair, Driv - ing out the gloom and sad - ness, Shedding sunlight ev - 'ry - where.

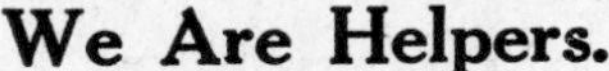

We Are Helpers. 119

MATTIE B. SHANNON. (P–J.) GRACE L. HOSMER.

mf *p* *pp*

1. All our Sav-iour's goodness show-ing, We are help-ers, will-ing help-ers;
2. Heart and hand His will o-bey-ing, We are help-ers, will-ing help-ers;
3. With a life of grate-ful prais-ing, We are help-ers, will-ing help-ers;

mf

With His love so bright-ly glow-ing, We are help-ers for our King.
Trust-ing Him to keep from stray-ing, We are help-ers for our King.
As our songs of love we're rais-ing, We are help-ers for our King.

CHORUS.

p *pp* *f*

We are help-ers, will-ing help-ers, In the sim-ple tasks we dai-ly find;

p *pp* *f*

We are help-ers, will-ing help-ers, With words and with deeds so kind.

Golden Rule Song. 120

MABEL E. LOCKER. (P–J.) C. AUSTIN MILES.

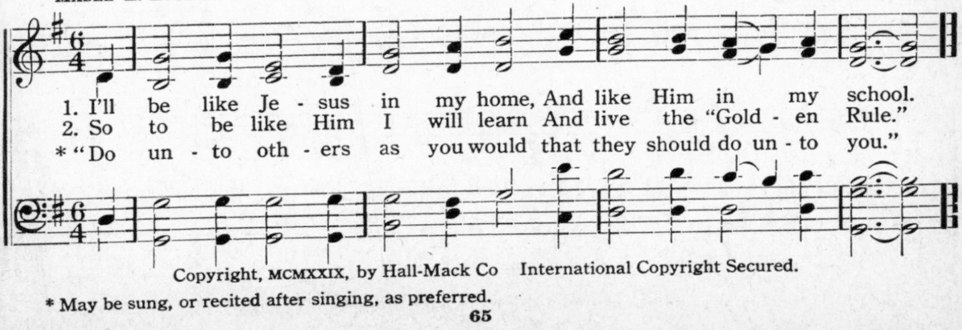

1. I'll be like Je-sus in my home, And like Him in my school.
2. So to be like Him I will learn And live the "Gold-en Rule."
* "Do un-to oth-ers as you would that they should do un-to you."

* May be sung, or recited after singing, as preferred.

121 His Helpers.

GRACE GORDON. (J.) J. LINCOLN HALL.

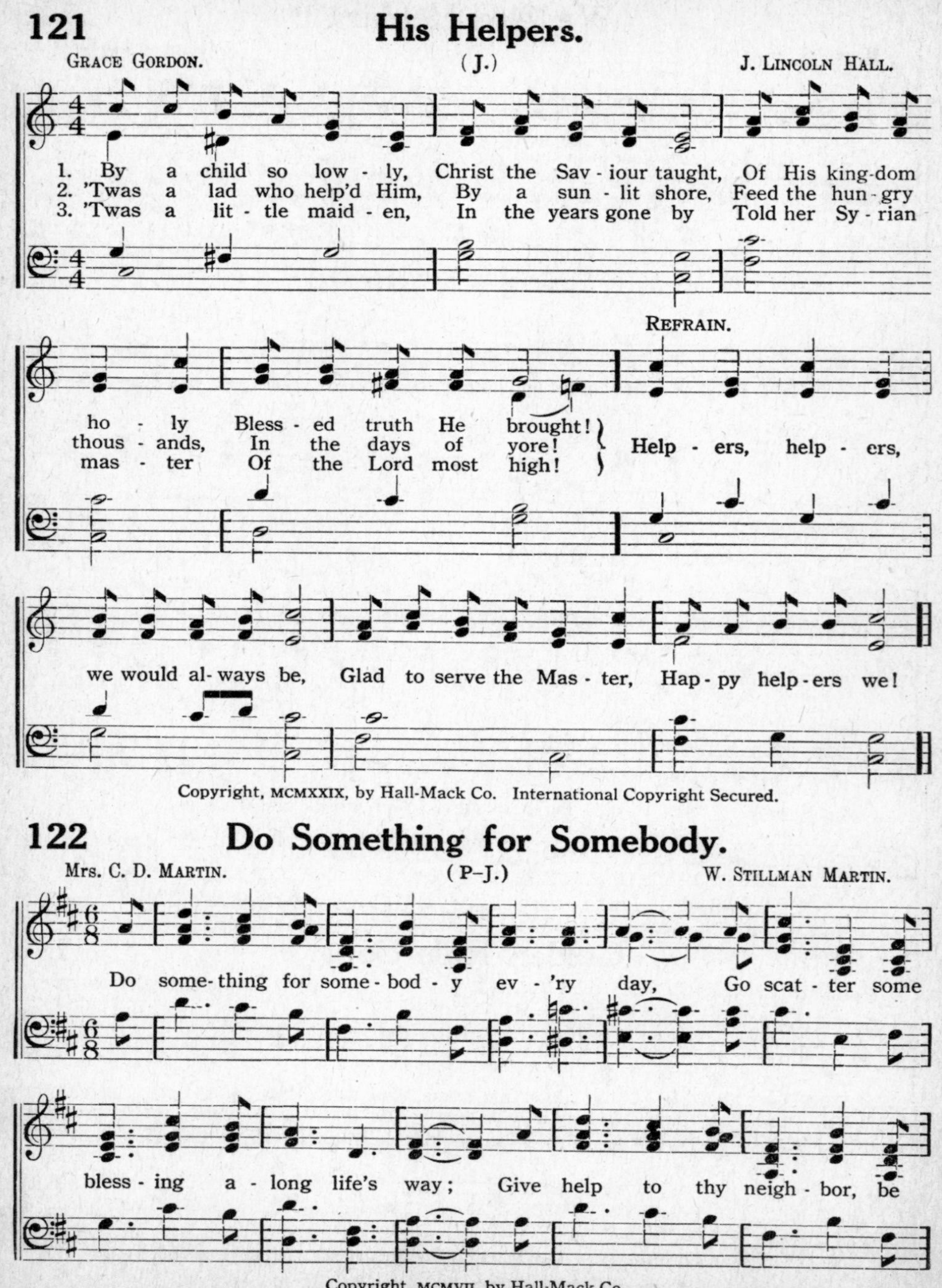
1. By a child so low - ly, Christ the Sav - iour taught, Of His king-dom ho - ly Bless - ed truth He brought!
2. 'Twas a lad who help'd Him, By a sun - lit shore, Feed the hun - gry thous - ands, In the days of yore!
3. 'Twas a lit - tle maid - en, In the years gone by Told her Sy - rian mas - ter Of the Lord most high!
REFRAIN.
Help - ers, help - ers, we would al - ways be, Glad to serve the Mas - ter, Hap - py help - ers we!

122 Do Something for Somebody.

Mrs. C. D. MARTIN. (P-J.) W. STILLMAN MARTIN.

Do some - thing for some - bod - y ev - 'ry day, Go scat - ter some bless - ing a - long life's way; Give help to thy neigh - bor, be

Do Something for Somebody.
watch-ful, pray; Do some-thing for some-bod-y ev-'ry day.
Doing Our Best.
123
MATTIE B. SHANNON.
(J.)
M. ISABELLE RITTER.
1. We will give to Christ the King Gifts of love, sweet and fair, Deeds for oth-ers we will bring, These He will share.
2. Not in sel-fish-ness and pride We will live, day by day, Serv-ing oth-ers by our side, Watch-ing our way.
3. In o-be-di-ence and love, Er-rands kind we will do, "In His name," Who reigns a-bove, Serv-ing a-new.
CHORUS.
We will do our best for Je-sus, Though our tal-ents be but small;
We will serve, though tasks be hum-ble, (Omit. . . . .)
Pledge we our best; He needs us all!

124 Why We Are Here.

C. R. F. (P–J.) CAROLYN R. FREEMAN.

1. Why am I here in this big old world? What does God want me to do?
2. Al - ways they say that the Sav - iour dear When He was here a - mong men,
3. None were too sin - ful to come to Christ, No mat - ter what they had done,
There is a rea - son for ev - 'ry-thing, A rea - son for me and for you.
Cared for the poor and the need - y ones, And helped them a - gain and a - gain.
Je - sus would free - ly for - give them all, And He would re - ceive ev - 'ry one.
CHORUS.
God wants me to be like Je - sus, To love and to serve here be - low;
He wants me to make this world bet - ter, So that is my mis - sion, I know.

125 O Master! When Thou Callest.

SARAH G. STOCK. (J.) HENRY SMART.

1. O Mas - ter! when Thou call - est, No voice may say Thee nay, For blest are they that
2. O Mas - ter! when Thou call - est, No heart may dare re - fuse; 'Tis hon - or, high - est

O Master! When Thou Callest.

fol - low Where Thou dost lead the way; In fresh - est prime of morn - ing, Or
hon - or, When Thou dost deign to use Our bright- est and our fair - est, Our
full- est glow of noon, The note of heav'nly warn- ing Can nev - er come too soon.
dear-est—all are Thine; Thou who for each one car - est, We hail Thy love's de- sign.
The Master's Garden.
126
C. R. F.
(P.)
Carolyn R. Freeman.
1. I know a love - ly gar - den, With - in this world of ours, With choic- est
2. The Mas - ter loves His gar - den, And wants each blos-som dear To fill the
Chorus.
lit - tle blos-soms, And love- ly blooming flow'rs.
world with beau-ty, And scat- ter joy and cheer.
It is the Mas-ter's gar-den, And
all the blossoms gay Are Je - sus' lit - tle chil-dren Who bloom for Him each day.

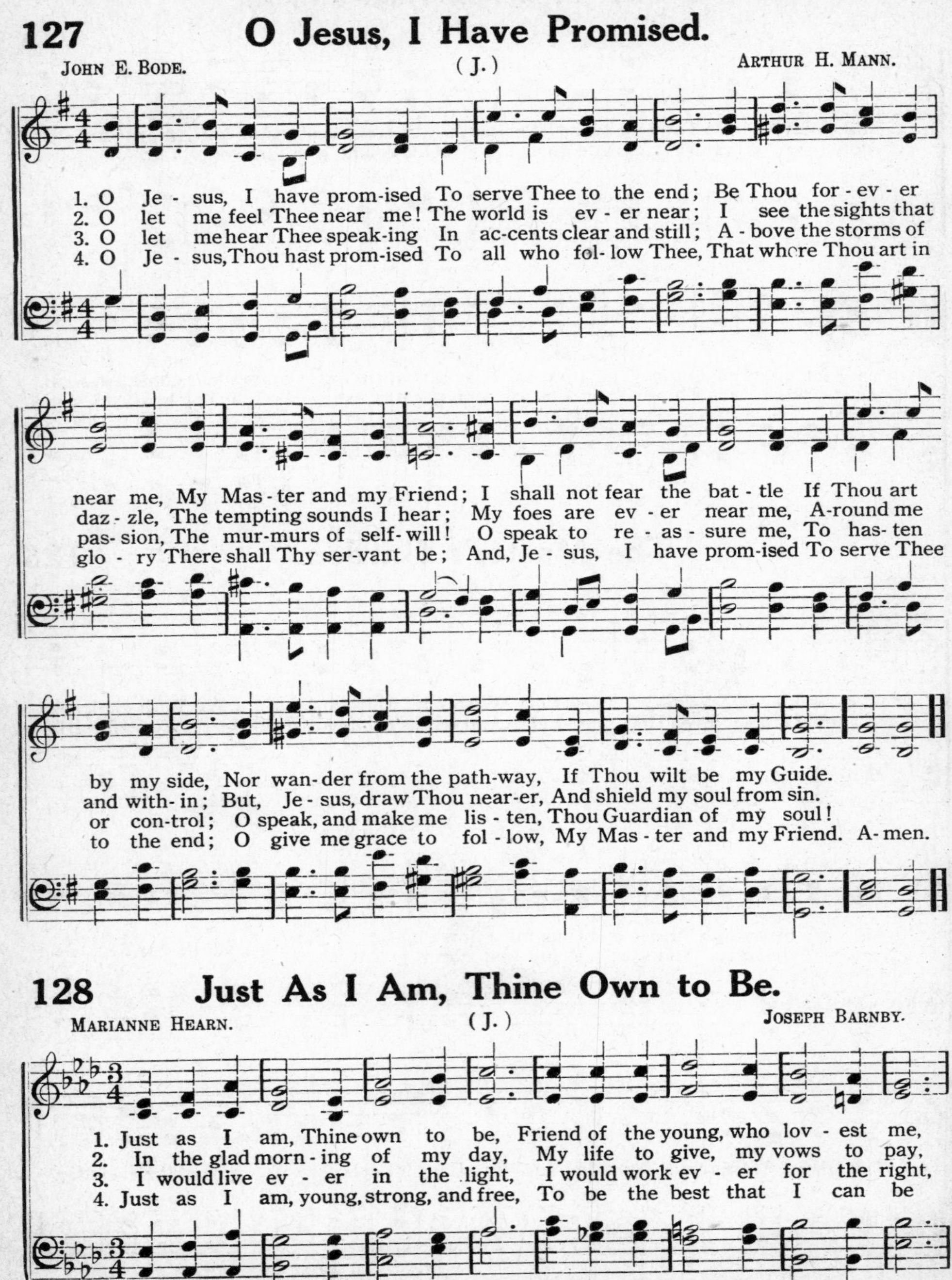
127 O Jesus, I Have Promised.
JOHN E. BODE.
(J.)
ARTHUR H. MANN.
1. O Je - sus, I have prom-ised To serve Thee to the end; Be Thou for - ev - er near me, My Mas - ter and my Friend; I shall not fear the bat - tle If Thou art by my side, Nor wan-der from the path-way, If Thou wilt be my Guide.
2. O let me feel Thee near me! The world is ev - er near; I see the sights that daz - zle, The tempting sounds I hear; My foes are ev - er near me, A-round me and with- in; But, Je - sus, draw Thou near-er, And shield my soul from sin.
3. O let me hear Thee speak-ing In ac-cents clear and still; A - bove the storms of pas- sion, The mur-murs of self- will! O speak to re - as - sure me, To has- ten or con-trol; O speak, and make me lis - ten, Thou Guardian of my soul!
4. O Je - sus, Thou hast prom-ised To all who fol- low Thee, That where Thou art in glo - ry There shall Thy ser-vant be; And, Je - sus, I have prom-ised To serve Thee to the end; O give me grace to fol - low, My Mas - ter and my Friend. A-men.
128 Just As I Am, Thine Own to Be.
MARIANNE HEARN.
(J.)
JOSEPH BARNBY.
1. Just as I am, Thine own to be, Friend of the young, who lov - est me,
2. In the glad morn - ing of my day, My life to give, my vows to pay,
3. I would live ev - er in the light, I would work ev - er for the right,
4. Just as I am, young, strong, and free, To be the best that I can be

Just As I Am, Thine Own to Be.

Unison.
To con-se-crate my-self to Thee. O Je-sus Christ I come.
With no re-serve and no de-lay, With all my heart I come.
I would serve Thee with all my might; Therefore, to Thee I come.
For truth, and right-eous-ness, and Thee, Lord of my life, I come. A-men.
Come Unto Me.
129
(J.)
A. A. Payn.
Come un-to me, all ye that la-bor, And are heav-y la-den and
I will give you rest. Take my yoke up-on you and learn of me,
For my yoke is eas-y and my bur-den is light, And ye shall find
rest un-to your souls, And ye shall find rest un-to your souls. A-men.

130 Lord, We Come to Thee.
C. R. F.
(P.)
Carolyn R. Freeman.
1. We are on - ly lit - tle chil-dren, And tho' youthful we may be,
2. Lit - tle chil-dren, lit - tle chil-dren Are the Mas-ter's jew - els fair.
3. Tho' we're on - ly lit - tle chil-dren, We be - long to Christ our King.
Christ the Sav - iour gen - tly calls us, "Lit - tle ones, come to me."
He will keep them, dai - ly keep them Safe in His ten - der care.
Hearts and hands in faith - ful serv - ice Un - to our Lord we bring.
Chorus.
Lord, we come, Lord, we come, In our child - hood's morn - ing;
Lord, we come, Lord, we come, Come to learn of Thee.
Copyright, MCMXXIX, by Hall-Mack Co. International Copyright Secured.
131 A Prayer.
(J.)
Clyde Willard.

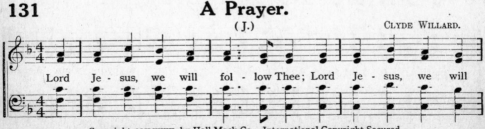

Lord Je - sus, we will fol - low Thee; Lord Je - sus, we will

A Prayer.

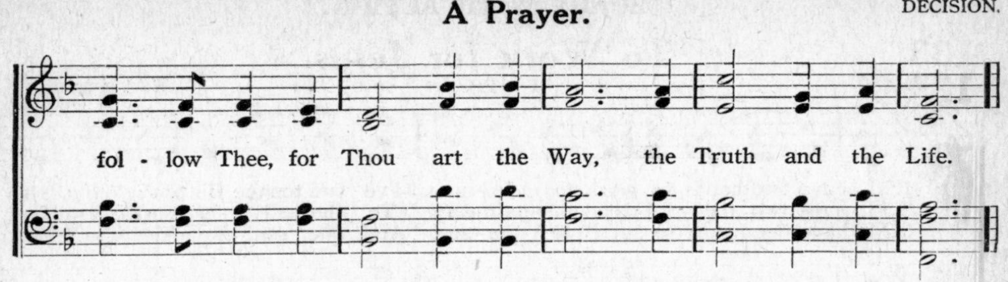
fol - low Thee, for Thou art the Way, the Truth and the Life.

Yes, the Lord Can Depend On Me. 132

ELSIE DUNCAN YALE. (J.) J. LINCOLN HALL.

1. There are fields that to har - vest are white, And a reap - er with joy I will be;
Golden sheaves will I bring, to my Mas - ter and King, For the Lord can de-pend on me!

2. There's a mes - sage to bear far and near, Of a Sav-iour whose love sets us free,
And the call ringing clear, glad of heart will I hear, For the Lord can de-pend on me!

3. There are souls who are drift - ing a - way, Let me bring them, dear Lord, unto thee.
I will seek them to-day, I will haste nor de-lay, For the Lord can de-pend on me!

CHORUS.

Yes, the Lord can de-pend on me, on me, Yes, the Lord can de-pend on me; on me:
And his name I'll confess, un- to him I say "yes," For the Lord can depend on me!

133 To Work for Jesus.

W. A. O. (P.) W. A. OGDEN.

1. [1]I have two hands to work for Je - sus, [2]I've one tongue His praise to tell;
2. [5]I have two feet to tread the path-way [6]To the heav'n - ly courts a - bove;
3. [8]I have one heart to give to Je - sus, And one soul for Him to save;

[3]I've two ears to hear His coun - sel, [4]And one voice a song to swell
[7]I've two eyes to read the Bi - ble, Tell - ing Je - sus' won-drous love.
Just one life for His dear serv - ice, And one self that He must have.

REFRAIN.

[9]Lord we come, Lord we come. In our child-hood's ear - ly morn - ing,
Lord we come, Lord we come, Come to learn of Thee.

1. Hold out hands. 2. Point to tongue. 3. Touch the ears. 4. Point to mouth. 5. Point to feet. 6. Point up. 7. Touch eyes. 8. Hand on heart. 9. Spread hands.

134 For Jesus.

A. A. PAYN. (B–P.) G. W. PAYN.

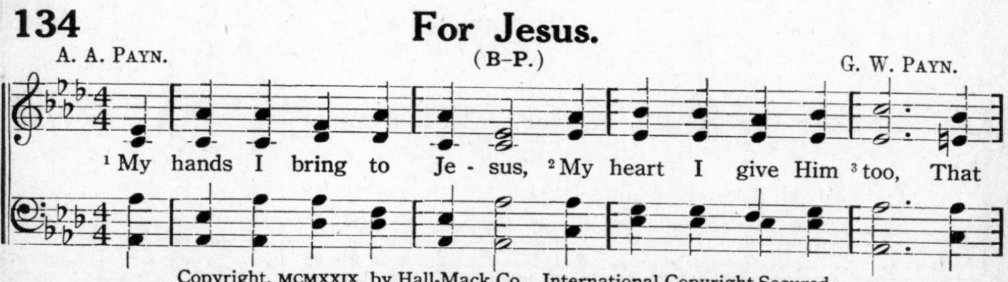
[1]My hands I bring to Je - sus, [2]My heart I give Him [3]too, That

1. Extend hands outward. 2. One hand over heart. 3. Both hands over heart. 4. Hands clasped, look up.

For Jesus.

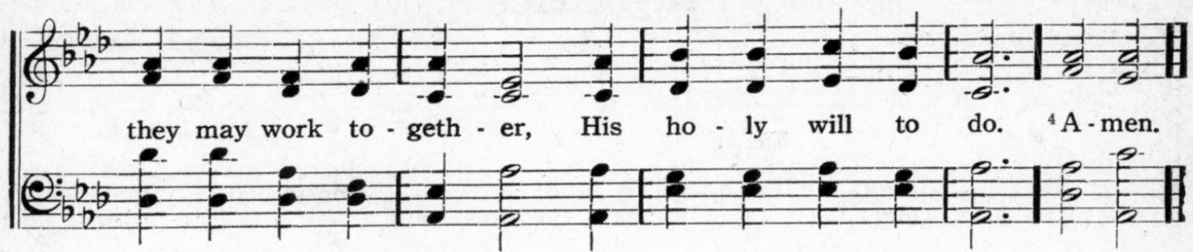
they may work to - geth - er, His ho - ly will to do. 4 A - men.

God Will Take Care of Us All. 135

C. R. F. (P.) CAROLYN R. FREEMAN.

1. 1 Out in the meadows the dais - ies sway; To and fro they light - ly go.
2. But - ter-flies yel - low, and glad, and bright, 7 Light - ly fly up in the sky,
3. Bob - o - links trill-ing a joy - ous song 9 Sing God's praise thro' gold - en days.

2 Hear what the dear lit - tle blos - soms say As they are mur - mur - ing low.
8 Tell - ing the world from the morn till night, 1 As they are flut - ter - ing by;
Sweet - ly they tell thro' the sum - mer long Of all His won - der - ful ways.

CHORUS.

3 "Trust in the Fa - ther what - e'er be - fall. 4 Look a - bove, God is love; And as He is 5 watching each spar - row small, 6 God will take care of us all."

1. Sway arms lightly to and fro, in good rhythm. 2. Bend forward with hand to ear in listening attitude. 3. Clasp hands as if in prayer. 4. Gesture and look upward. 5. Bend forward, shading eyes with hands. 6. Fold arms on chest and look upward in attitude of trust. 7. Raise arms, palms downward, swaying them lightly from side to side, fluttering fingers. 8. Hold out both arms toward audience. 9. Point upward.

136 My Clock.

MATTIE B. SHANNON. (P.) GRACE L. HOSMER.

1. [1] Hear the queer, queer tick - ing of my great big clock, There's a mes - sage for each day,[2] As it tells [3] the time with a ring - ing chime, On the Sabbath this it seems to say:
2. It's the strang - est [5] thing how it will hur - ry on When I [6] need to hur - ry, too; And it seems to say, "You'll be late [7] to - day, And the pleasant songs will all be thro'!"
3. Tho' I watch [8] it close - ly ev - 'ry now and then, O it nev - er seems to rest; And [9] the pen - du - lum with a hap - py hum, Seems to whisper, "Do your ver - y best!"
CHORUS.
[4] "Tick, tock, now has come the Sabbath day, Tick, tock, time to rest from work and play;
Tick, tock, tick, tock, haste to Sunday School, Tick, tock, tick, tock, that's the Sabbath rule;"

My Clock.

O I think it is quite clear That my clock is ver - y, ver - y queer.

1. Hand back of ear in attitude of listening. 2. Both hands extended outward at sides. 3. Keep time to music with right hand moving up and down. 4. Move index finger of right hand up and down as each "Tick, tock" is said. 5. Shake head slowly. 6. Right hand on chest. 7. Shake head from side to side. 8. Look up. 9. Move right hand from right to left in time to music.

Little Eyes. 137

Dr. C. R. BLACKALL. (P.) W. H. DOANE.

1. Lit - tle eyes,[1] lit - tle eyes, Soft - ly close in wor - ship now;
2. Lit - tle ears,[4] lit - tle ears, Lis - ten while He speaks to you;[3]
3. Lit - tle heart,[6] lit - tle heart, Read - y be to take Him in;[7]

Fold the arms,[2] bow the head,[3] While we whis - per soft and low,
Gen - tle words, full of peace, Come to those who love Him true;[2]
Lit - tle hands,[8] bus - y be, Oth - er hearts for Christ to win;

Slower.

God is here, and hap - py we, In His pres - ence e'er may be.
God is love, and we must be Lit - tle fol - l'wers glad and free.[5]
God will help you ev - 'ry day, Guide you in His bless - ed[9] way.

Used by permission.

1. Touch eyes. 2. Fold arms. 3. Bow heads. 4. Touch ears. 5. Raise hands. 6. Right hand over heart 7. Spread hands and arms. 8. Wave hands from side to side. 9. Point upward with fore-finger of right hand.

138 Hurry, Mr. Clock.

ALICE JEAN CLEATOR. (P.) C. AUSTIN MILES.

1. Tick,[1] tock, tick, tock, tick, tock, tick, tock, Lis - ten to old Mis - ter Clock!
2. When it's sum- mer time so dear, Va - ca-tion time then is here,
3. Dear me,[4] we can scarce-ly wait, O how you ex - as - per - ate!
rit.
Tick - ing all the hours a - way, Till the * mer - ry Christ- mas day!
And you tick the hours [3] so fast, From the first one to the last!
Hur - ry, Mis - ter Clock and say, "Mer - ry, [5] mer - ry Christ- mas day!"
CHORUS.
p
f
With your tick, tock, tick, tock, tick, tock, tick, tock, Please hur-ry [2] up, Mis-ter Clock;
O you count the hours so slow! Can't you make them fast - er, fast - er go?
p
f
With your tick, tock, tick, tock, tick, tock, tick, tock, Please hurry up, Mis- ter Clock.

* Or "Happy holiday" for general use.

1. Motion with fore-finger as if representing pendulum of clock. 2. Stamp foot. 3. Motion as if counting on fingers. 4. Hands clasped in impatience. 5. Hands extended, smiling.

The World Children for Jesus. 139

M. C. B. (P.) MARGARET COOTE BROWN.

Legato, with expression.
1. The cun-ning pa-poose in the wig-wam that lives, Whose life is so hap-py and free, Is my In-di-an broth-er; and Je-sus loves him Just as He loves you and me.........
2. The Es-ki-mo ba-bies are wrapped all in fur; They live in the north coun-try Where cold winds blow; and Je-sus loves them Just
3. The lit-tle Jap ba-bies, with shin-ing, dark eyes, Live on a green isle in the sea: Too man-y to count; and Je-sus loves them Just
4. The pret-ty brown ba-bies who roll in the sand, In a coun-try far o-ver the sea, Are my Af-ri-can brothers; and Je-sus loves them Just
5. And all the dear ba-bies, wher-ev-er they grow, So cun-ning, so pre-cious, so wee, Are God's dar-ling children; and Je-sus loves them Just
REFRAIN. Sostenuto.
The world chil-dren for Je-sus, The world chil-dren for Je-sus,......... The world chil-dren for Je-sus who loves them, Who loves ev-'ry one............
ff
dim.

140 Jesus Loves the Little Children.
Rev. C. H. Woolston, D. D.
(P.)
Geo. F. Root.
1. Je - sus calls the chil - dren dear, "Come to me and nev - er fear, For I
2. Je - sus is the Shep - herd true, And He'll al - ways stand by you, For He
3. I am com - ing, Lord, to Thee. And Thy sol - dier I will be, For He
love the lit - tle chil - dren of the world. I will take you by the hand,
loves the lit - tle chil - dren of the world. He's a Sav - iour great and strong,
loves the lit - tle chil - dren of the world. And His cross I'll al - ways bear,
D. S.—yel - low, black and white,
Fine.
Lead you to the bet - ter land, For I love the lit - tle chil - dren of the world.
And He'll shield you from the wrong, For He loves the lit - tle chil - dren of the world.
And for Him I'll do and dare, For He loves the lit - tle chil - dren of the world
They are pre - cious in His sight, Je - sus loves the lit - tle chil - dren of the world.
Chorus.
Je - sus loves the lit - tle chil - dren, All the children of the world; Red and
lit - tle children, All the chil - dren of the world;
Used by permission of Mrs. C. H. Woolston, owner.
141 Boys and Girls of Every Color.
Mabel E. Locker.
(B-P.)
C. Austin Miles.
1. Boys and girls of ev - 'ry col - or, Je - sus loves you, Je - sus
2. Boys and girls of ev - 'ry col - or, We all love you, we all

Boys and Girls of Every Color.
loves you; Black and White and Red and Yel - low, Je - sus loves you.
love you; Black and White and Red and Yel - low, We all love you.
O Zion, Haste, Thy Mission High Fulfilling. 142
Mary Ann Thomson.
(J.)
James Walch.
1. O Zi - on, haste thy mis - sion high ful - fill - ing, To tell to all the world that God is Light, That He who made all na - tions is not will - ing One soul should per - ish, lost in shades of night.
2. Be - hold how ma - ny thou - sands still are ly - ing Bound in the dark - some pris on - house of sin, With none to tell them of the Sav - iour's dy - ing, Or of the life He died for them to win.
3. Pro - claim to ev - 'ry peo - ple, tongue and na - tion That God, in whom they live and move, is Love; Tell how He stooped to save His lost cre - a - tion, And died on earth that man might live a - bove.
4. Give of thy sons to bear the mes - sage glo - rious; Give of thy wealth to speed them on their way; Pour out thy soul for them in pray'r vic - to - rious; And all thou send - est Je - sus will re - pay.
5. He comes a - gain: O Zi - on, ere thou meet Him, Make known to ev - 'ry heart His sav - ing grace: Let none whom He hath ransomed fail to greet Him, Thro' thy ne - glect, un - fit to see His face.
Refrain.
Pub - lish glad ti - dings, ti - dings of peace, Ti - dings of Je - sus, re - demp - tion and re - lease.

143 Little Children Far Away.

ELIZABETH WOOD. (P–J.) MAURICE A. CLIFTON.

1. Lit - tle chil - dren far a - way, Lov - ing gifts we bring to - day;
2. Lit - tle chil - dren far a - way, Je - sus calls, His word o - bey;
3. Lit - tle chil - dren far a - way, For you we will work and pray;

That of Je - sus you may learn, And to Christ the Sav - iour turn.
Hear and heed His lov - ing call, For He loves the chil - dren all.
And our gifts we'll glad - ly send, Tell - ing you of Christ our Friend.

CHORUS.

Lit - tle chil - dren far a - way. Lov - ing gifts we're bring - ing;
That you too may know our Friend, And His praise be sing - ing.

NOTE:—This may be sung as foreign missionary offerings are received. Pictures of children of foreign lands may be shown, after the song is sung.

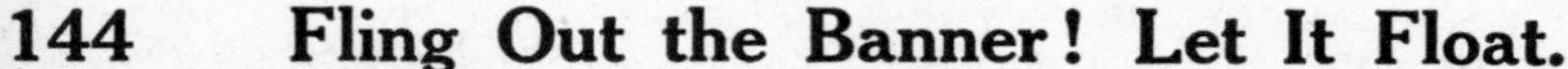

144 Fling Out the Banner! Let It Float.

Bishop GEORGE W. DOANE. (J.) J. BAPTISTE CALKIN.

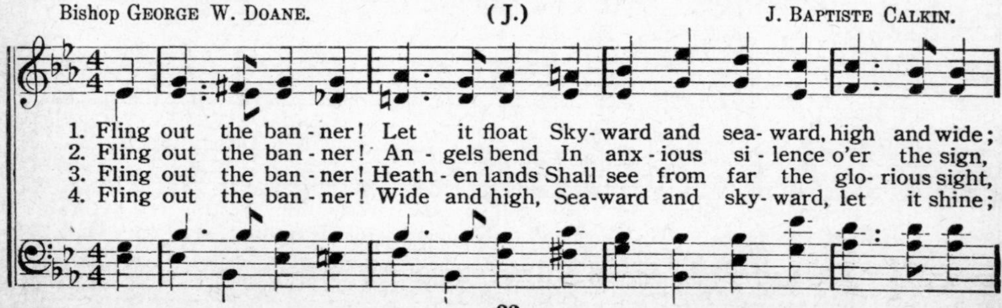
1. Fling out the ban - ner! Let it float Sky - ward and sea - ward, high and wide;
2. Fling out the ban - ner! An - gels bend In anx - ious si - lence o'er the sign,
3. Fling out the ban - ner! Heath - en lands Shall see from far the glo - rious sight,
4. Fling out the ban - ner! Wide and high, Sea - ward and sky - ward, let it shine;

Fling Out the Banner! Let It Float.

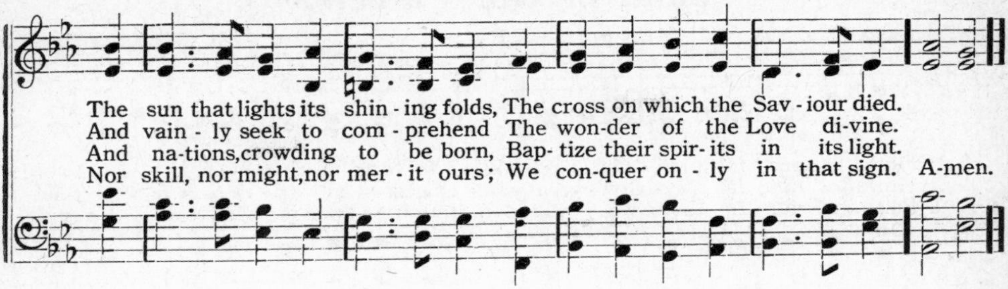

The sun that lights its shin - ing folds, The cross on which the Sav - iour died.
And vain - ly seek to com - prehend The won-der of the Love di-vine.
And na-tions, crowding to be born, Bap- tize their spir- its in its light.
Nor skill, nor might, nor mer - it ours; We con-quer on - ly in that sign. A-men.

From Greenland's Icy Mountains. 145

REGINALD HEBER. (J.) LOWELL MASON.

1. From Greenland's i - cy moun - tains, From In - dia's cor - al strand,
2. Waft, waft, ye winds, His sto - ry, And you, ye wa - ters, roll,

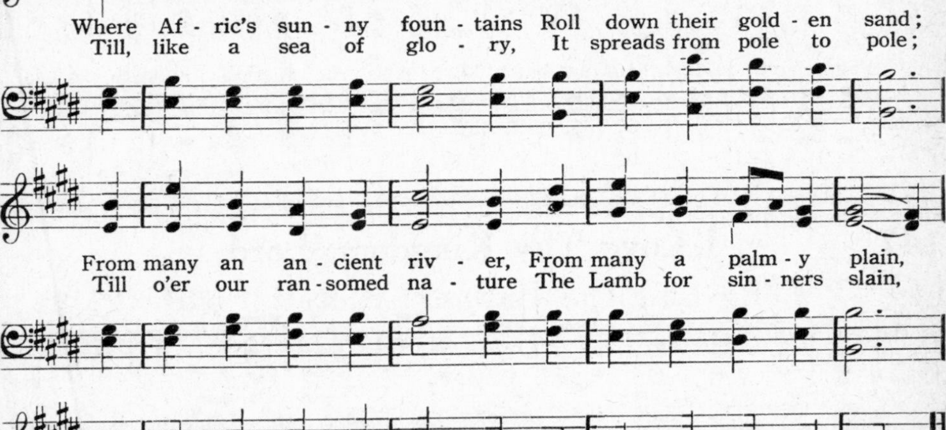
Where Af - ric's sun - ny foun - tains Roll down their gold - en sand;
Till, like a sea of glo - ry, It spreads from pole to pole;
From many an an - cient riv - er, From many a palm - y plain,
Till o'er our ran - somed na - ture The Lamb for sin - ners slain,

They call us to de - liv - er Their land from er - ror's chain.
Re - deem - er, King, Cre - a - tor, In bliss re - turns to reign.

146 Faith of Our Fathers.
Frederick W. Faber. (J.) H. F. Hemy, adpt.
1. Faith of our fa - thers! Liv - ing still In spite of dun - geon, fire and sword:
2. Faith of our fa - thers, God's great pow'r Shall soon all na - tions win for thee;
3. Faith of our fa - thers, we will love Both friend and foe in all our strife,
O how our hearts beat high with joy, When-e'er we hear that glo - rious word:
And thro' the truth that comes from God Mankind shall then be tru - ly free.
And preach thee, too, as love knows how, By kind - ly words and vir - tuous life.
Faith of our fa - thers! Ho - ly faith! We will be true to thee till death. A-men.
147 I Love Thy Kingdom, Lord.
Timothy Dwight. (J.) Aaron Williams, Coll.
1. I love Thy king - dom, Lord, The house of Thine a - bode, The
2. I love Thy church, O God! Her walls be - fore Thee stand, Dear
3. For her my tears shall fall; For her my pray'rs as - cend; To
4. Be - yond my high - est joy I prize her heav'n - ly ways, Her
5. Sure as Thy truth shall last, To Zi - on shall be giv'n The

I Love Thy Kingdom, Lord.

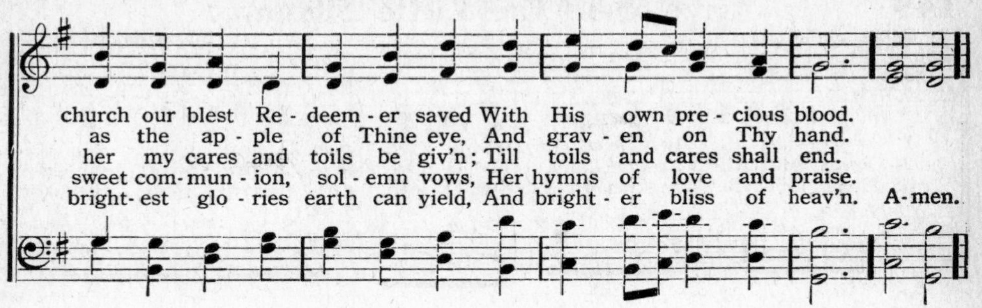
church our blest Re - deem - er saved With His own pre - cious blood.
as the ap - ple of Thine eye, And grav - en on Thy hand.
her my cares and toils be giv'n; Till toils and cares shall end.
sweet com - mun - ion, sol - emn vows, Her hymns of love and praise.
bright - est glo - ries earth can yield, And bright - er bliss of heav'n. A - men.

The Church's One Foundation. 148

Rev. Samuel J. Stone. (J.) Samuel S. Wesley.

1. The Church's one Foun - da - tion Is Je - sus Christ her Lord; She is His new cre -
2. E - lect from ev - 'ry na - tion, Yet one o'er all the earth, Her char - ter of sal -
3. 'Mid toil and trib - u - la - tion, And tu - mult of her war, She waits the con - sum -
4. Yet she on earth hath un - ion With God the Three in One, And mys - tic sweet com -

a - tion By wa - ter and the word: From heav'n He came and sought her To be His
va - tion One Lord, one faith, one birth; One ho - ly Name she bless - es, Par - takes one
ma - tion Of peace for - ev - er - more; Till with the vis - ion glo - rious Her long - ing
mun - ion With those whose rest is won: O hap - py ones and ho - ly! Lord, give us

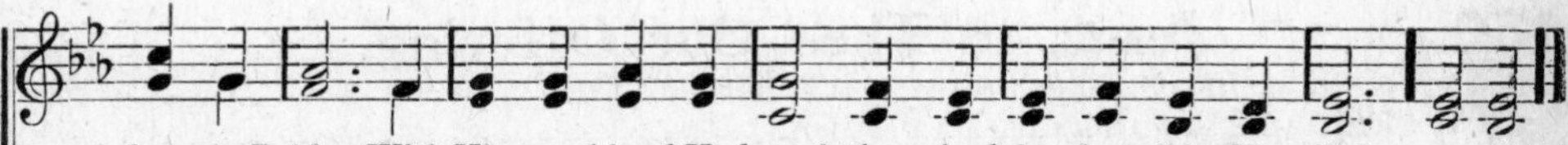

ho - ly Bride: With His own blood He bought her, And for her life He died.
ho - ly food, And to one hope she press - es, With ev - 'ry grace en - dued.
eyes are blest, And the great Church vic - to - rious Shall be the Church at rest.
grace that we, Like them the meek and low - ly, On high may dwell with Thee. A - men.

149 Give, Said the Little Stream.
FANNY J. CROSBY.
(P.)
WM. B. BRADBURY.
1. Give, said the lit - tle stream, Give, O give, give, O give, Give, said the lit - tle stream, As it hur - ried down the hill; I'm small I know, but wher - ev - er I go, The fields grow green - er still.
2. Give, said the lit - tle rain, Give, O give, give, O give, Give, said the lit - tle rain As it fell up - on the flow'rs; I'll raise their droop - ing heads a - gain, As it fell up - on the flow'rs.
3. Give, then, for Je - sus give; Give, O give, give, O give, Give, then, for Je - sus give; There is something all can give, Do as the streams and blos - soms do, For God and oth - ers live.
CHORUS.
Sing - ing, sing - ing, all the day, Give a - way, O give a - way, Give, O give a - way.
1
2
150 Jesus, to Thee Our Offering.
(P-J.)
Je - sus, to Thee our of - fer - ing With glad and thank - ful hearts we bring,

Jesus, to Thee Our Offering.

Thy blessing give, dear Lord, for we And all we have, be - long to Thee. A - men.

Offertory Sentence. 151

C. A. M. (J.) C. Austin Miles.

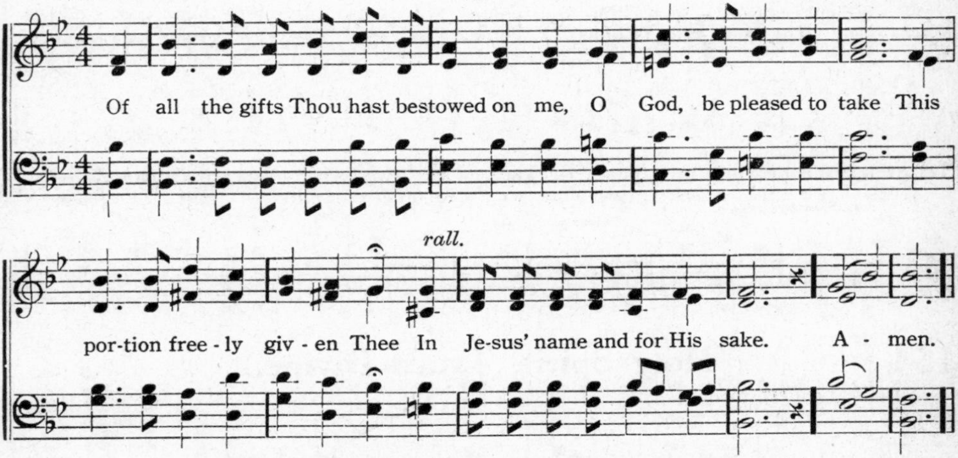

Of all the gifts Thou hast bestowed on me, O God, be pleased to take This

rall.

por-tion free - ly giv - en Thee In Je-sus' name and for His sake. A - men.

We Give Thee but Thine Own.
152
William Walsham How.
(P–J.)
Joseph Barnby.
We give Thee but Thine own, What - e'er the gift may be; All
that we have is Thine a - lone, A trust, O Lord, from Thee. A - men.

153 Holy Spirit, Faithful Guide.
M. M. W. Alt.
(J.)
M. M. Wells.
Fine.
1. Ho - ly Spir - it faith - ful Guide, Ev - er near the Chris-tian's side;
Gen - tly lead us by the hand, Pil - grims in an earth - ly land;
2. Ev - er pres - ent, tru - est Friend, Ev - er near Thine aid to lend,
Thou wilt leave us not a - lone, But wilt make Thy pres - ence known.
D.C.—Whisp'ring soft - ly, "Chil - dren, come, Fol - low Me, I'll guide thee home."
D.C.—And Thy gen - tle "Come, O come, Fol - low Me, I'll guide thee home."
D.C.
Make our hearts in Thee re - joice, As we lis - ten for Thy voice,
As we old - er grow may we Learn more ful - ly still of Thee,
154 Holy Spirit, Truth Divine.
Samuel Longfellow.
(J.)
Gottschalk.
1. Ho - ly Spir - it, Truth di - vine, Dawn up - on this soul of mine;
2. Ho - ly Spir - it, Love di - vine, Glow with - in this heart of mine;
3. Ho - ly Spir - it, Pow'r di - vine, Fill and nerve this will of mine;
4. Ho - ly Spir - it, Joy di - vine, Glad - den Thou this heart of mine;
Word of God, and in - ward Light, Wake my spir - it, clear my sight.
Kin - dle ev - 'ry high de - sire; Per - ish self in Thy pure fire.
By Thee may I strong - ly live, Brave - ly bear, and no - bly strive.
In the des - ert ways I sing, "Spring, O Well, for - ev - er spring!" A-men.

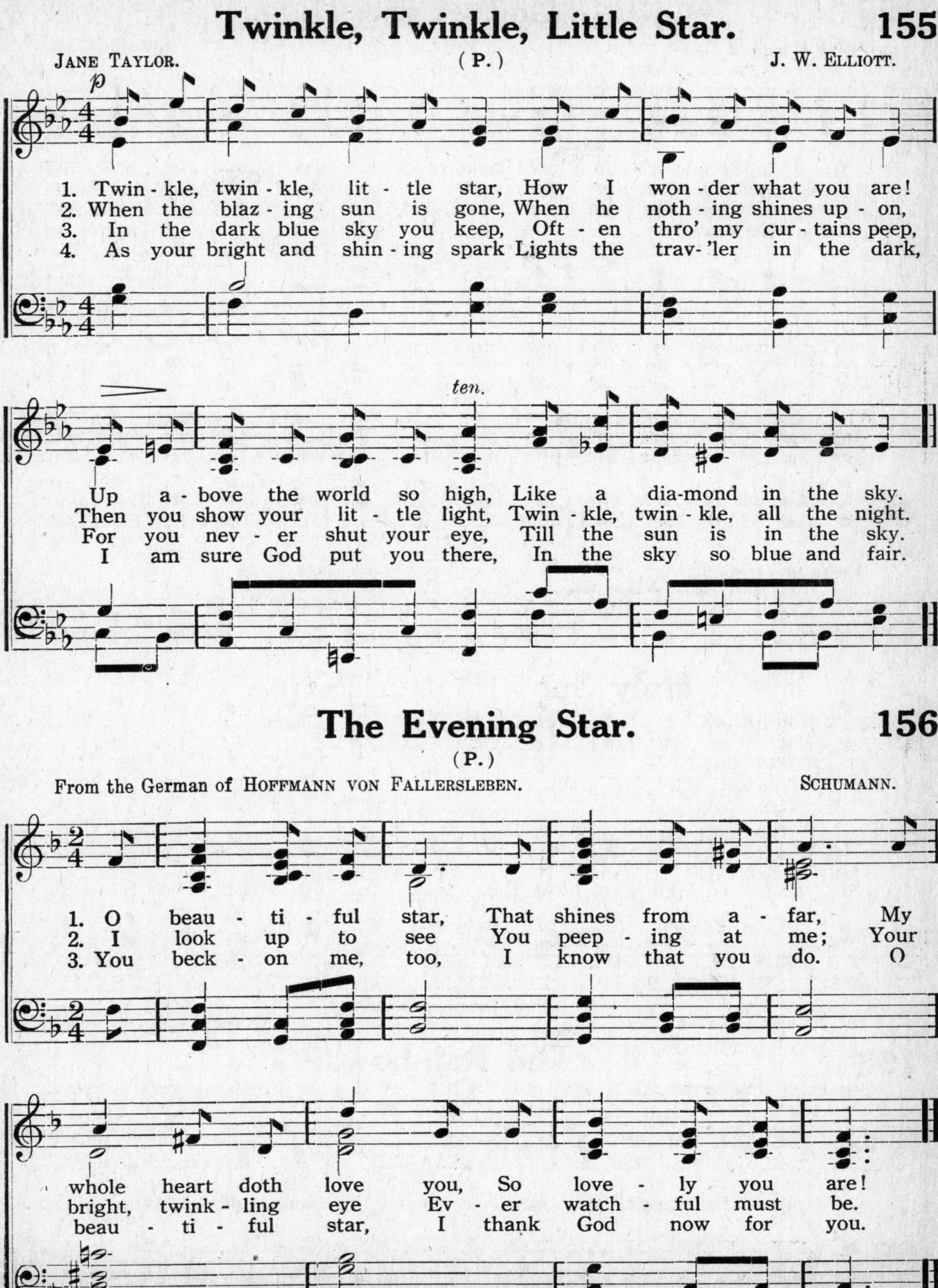
Twinkle, Twinkle, Little Star. 155
(P.)
JANE TAYLOR.
J. W. ELLIOTT.
p
1. Twin - kle, twin - kle, lit - tle star, How I won - der what you are!
2. When the blaz - ing sun is gone, When he noth - ing shines up - on,
3. In the dark blue sky you keep, Oft - en thro' my cur - tains peep,
4. As your bright and shin - ing spark Lights the trav- 'ler in the dark,
ten.
Up a - bove the world so high, Like a dia-mond in the sky.
Then you show your lit - tle light, Twin - kle, twin - kle, all the night.
For you nev - er shut your eye, Till the sun is in the sky.
I am sure God put you there, In the sky so blue and fair.
The Evening Star. 156
(P.)
From the German of HOFFMANN VON FALLERSLEBEN.
SCHUMANN.
1. O beau - ti - ful star, That shines from a - far, My
2. I look up to see You peep - ing at me; Your
3. You beck - on me, too, I know that you do. O
whole heart doth love you, So love - ly you are!
bright, twink - ling eye Ev - er watch - ful must be.
beau - ti - ful star, I thank God now for you.

157
God's Care.
JANE TAYLOR.
(P–J.)
HOWARD CLARE.
Verse may be sung as a Solo by a little girl.
1. Who taught the birds to build their nests Of wool and hay and moss?
2. Who taught the bus - y bee to fly A - mong the sweet - est flow'rs,
3. Who taught the lit - tle ant the way Her nar - row hole to bore,
Who taught them how to weave it best, And lay the twigs a - cross?
And lay her store of hon - ey by, To eat in win - ter hours?
And through the pleas - ant sum - mer day, To gath - er up her store?
CHORUS.
'Twas God who taught them all the way, And gave them all their skill:
He teach - es chil - dren, when they pray, To do His ho - ly will.
Hall-Mack Co., owner.
158
The Rainbow.
CHRISTINA G. ROSSETTI.
(B.)
Adapted from SCHUMANN.
If all were rain and nev - er sun, No bow could span the hill;
Con Pedale.

The Rainbow.

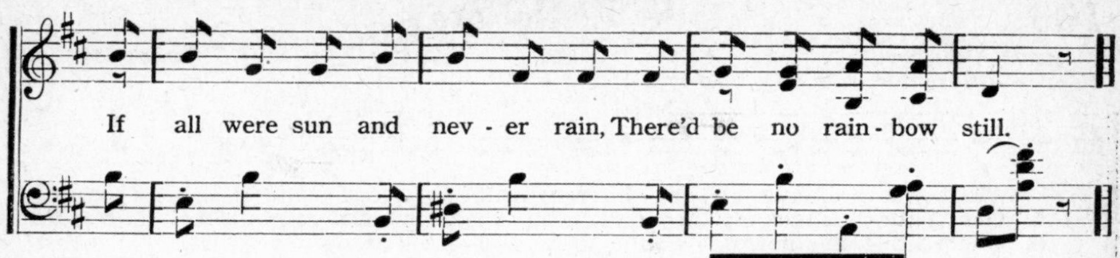

If all were sun and never rain, There'd be no rainbow still.

The Months of the Year. 159

MATTIE B. SHANNON. (P–J.) ALICE L. WOODCOCK.

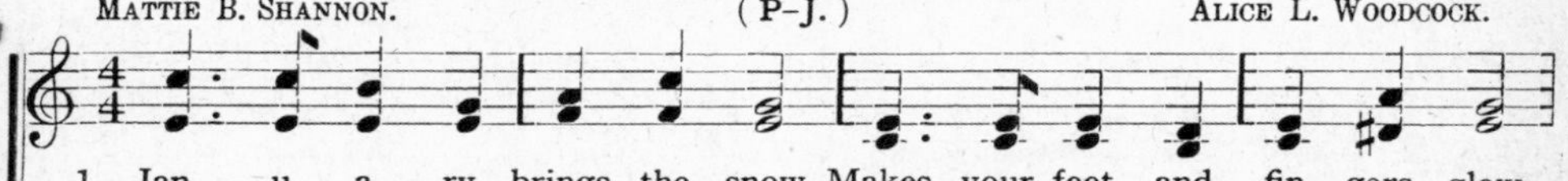

1. Jan - u - a - ry brings the snow, Makes your feet and fin - gers glow,
2. May 'neath skies of bright - est hue Gleams with sign of life a - new;
3. In Sep - tem - ber gold - en - rod Gleams like sun - shine sent from God;

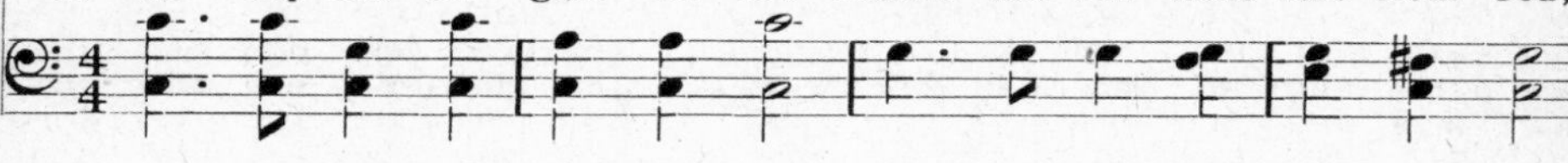

Feb - ru - a - ry brings the rain, Thaws the fro - zen lakes a - gain;
June brings tu - lips, lil - ies, ro - ses, Fills the chil - dren's hands with po - sies:
Fresh Oc - to - ber brings the pheas - ant, Then to gath - er nuts is pleasant;

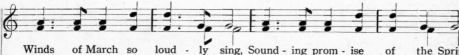

Winds of March so loud - ly sing, Sound - ing prom - ise of the Spring;
When Ju - ly burns hill and plain, God sends cool - ing show'rs a - gain;
Down No - vem - ber's chil - ly way Comes the glad Thanks - giv - ing Day;

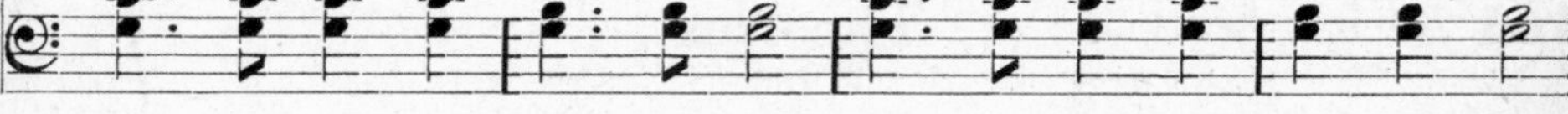

A - pril brings the blos - soms fair, Sym - bol of a Fa - ther's care.
Au - gust brings the sheaves of corn, Then the har - vest home is born.
Cold De - cem - ber is the time Christ - mas bells a mes - sage chime.

160 One Little Star.

SUSAN COOLIDGE. (P.) Gascon Carol.

Allegretto.

1. One lit - tle star in the star - ry night, One lit - tle
2. One lit - tle flow'r in the flow - er - ful spring One lit - tle
3. Each lit - tle star has its spe - cial ray, Each lit - tle
4. Each lit - tle child can some love - work find, Each lit - tle

beam in the noon - day light, One lit - tle drop in the
feath - er in one lit - tle wing, One lit - tle note when the
beam has its place in the day, Each lit - tle riv - er drop
hand and each lit - tle...... mind, All can be gen - tle and

riv - er's might, What can they do,...... O what can they do?
man - y birds sing, All are so lit - tle, fee - ble and few.
im - pulse and sway; Feath - er and flow - er and song - let help too.
use - ful and kind, Though they are lit - tle like me and like you.

161 The Nest.

(Let the children join hands and form a circle to represent hedge, two of the smallest being chosen for the eggs, and kneeling in the center. In the second verse they raise their heads and sing the "peeps," while all the children join in the last line.)

FRIEDRICH FROEBEL. (B.) Russian Folk-song.

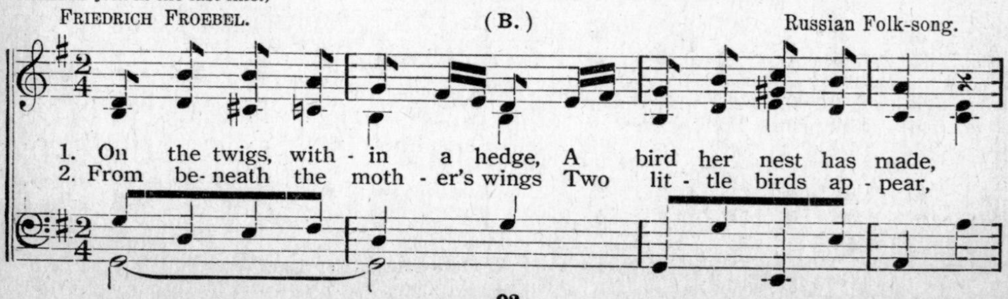
1. On the twigs, with - in a hedge, A bird her nest has made,
2. From be-neath the moth - er's wings Two lit - tle birds ap - pear,

The Nest.
In the nest so soft and warm Two ti - ny eggs are laid.
Hear them cry - ing, "Peep, peep, peep, We love you, moth - er dear."
Flowers.
162
Frances Ridley Havergal.
(J.)
Alberto Randegger.
1. Buds and bells, sweet A - pril pleas-ures, Spring-ing all a - round,.........
2. When the wea - ry lit - tle flow - ers Close their star-ry eyes,..........
3. Then He gives the pleas-ant weath - er, Sun-shine warm and free,..........
4. Though He can - not hear you sing - ing Soft - ly chim-ing lays,..........
White and gold and crim - son treas- ures, From the cold, un - love - ly ground.
By the dark and dew - y hours, Strength and fresh - ness God sup- plies.
Mak - ing all things glad to - geth - er Kind to them and kind to me.
Sure - ly God can see you bring - ing Si - lent songs of word- less praise;
He who gave them grace and hue, Made the lit - tle chil-dren too.
He who sends the gen - tle dew, Cares for lit - tle chil-dren too.
Love - ly flow'rs, He lov - eth you, And He loves the chil-dren too.
Hears your an - them, sweet and true, And He hears the chil-dren too.

163 Sun and Rain.

A. A. Payn.
(B–P.)
H. J. Lacey.
1. Drop-ping, 1drop-ping falls the rain From the 2sky, Gaz-ing thro' the win-dow 3pane, We won-der why?
2. Shin-ing, 4shin-ing, comes the sun, All the day, But when all his work is done, He hides 5a-way.
3. Flow-ers 6bloom in sweet con-tent On the plain; They know why the 7Lord has sent the sun and rain.
Chorus.
Ev-'ry-where, 8flow-ers fair, Shed 9their fra-grance on the air Ev-'ry day, prais-ing 10God, For His 11care.

1. Raise hands. bring down, moving fingers. 2. Look up. 3. Hand over eyes as if gazing. 4. Both hands extended out and up. 5. Cover eyes with both hands. 6. Both hands extended, wave to and fro, palms down. 7. Look up. 8. Arms stretched out from side. 9. Point down with left hand. 10. Point up with right hand. 11. Bring hands down.

164 Little Raindrops.

(B.)

1. Lit-tle rain-drops fall-ing down, Fall-ing down, fall-ing down,
2. Lit-tle bird-ies in the air, Fly-ing 'round, fly-ing 'round;

NOTE—Teacher will instruct, with appropriate gestures.

Little Raindrops.

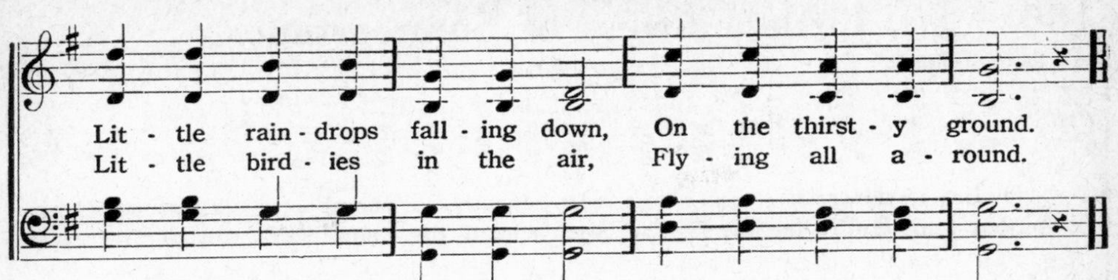
Lit - tle rain - drops fall - ing down, On the thirst - y ground.
Lit - tle bird - ies in the air, Fly - ing all a - round.

God Knows What is Best for You. 165

C. R. F. (P.) CAROLYN R. FREEMAN.

1. When the skies are bright and blue, In the sun - ny weath - er,
2. All the lit - tle blos - soms small Col - ors bright are show - ing;
3. Ev - 'ry lit - tle cloud of gray Has a sil - ver lin - ing;

'Tis an eas - y thing to do To be glad to - geth - er.
If the rain should nev - er fall They would soon stop grow - ing.
Oft - en on a rain - y day There's a rain - bow shin - ing.

CHORUS.

{But when at morn you rise to find it rain - ing, Tho' the clouds may
{Just trust in God. Keep on with - out complain - ing, (*Omit*............

1

hide your sky of blue,

2

God the Fa - ther knows what is best for you.

166 Little Flowers of Summertime.

GRACE GORDON. (P.) CLYDE WILLARD.

1. Lit - tle flow'rs of summer-time, Sleep beneath the snow! Win-ter comes with
2. Lit - tle flow'rs,'tis time to rest, Sleep beneath the snow! On the warm earth's
frost and rime, Sleep beneath the snow! For the Fa-ther loves you all,
kind - ly breast, Sleep beneath the snow! To the Fa-ther you are dear,
Flow - ers low - ly, flow - ers small, Till you hark the blue-bird's call,
And His care is al - ways near, Thro' the days so cold and drear,
REFRAIN.
Sleep be-neath the snow! (Hum.........) Go to sleep! Sleep be-neath the
snow! (Hum............) Go to sleep! Sleep be - neath the snow!
p

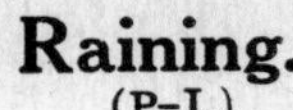
Raining.

A. H. A. (P–J.) A. H. Ackley.

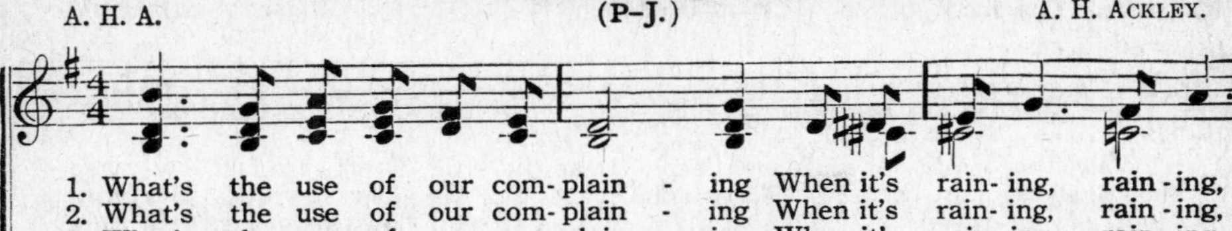
1. What's the use of our com- plain - ing When it's rain- ing, rain - ing,
2. What's the use of our com- plain - ing When it's rain- ing, rain - ing,
3. What's the use of our com- plain - ing When it's rain- ing, rain - ing,

rain - ing? God has will'd the rain, so let it be, He knows
rain - ing? Flow'rs must drink the wa - ter if they grow, Streams must
rain - ing? Think of all the bless-ings it will bring, Look your

Chorus.
what is best for you and me.
car - ry wa- ter if they flow.
sun - ni - est and smile and sing.
It's a - rain-ing rain, it's a - rain-ing rain,

Hear it pat- ter on the win - dow pane; It's a - rain-ing rain, It's a -

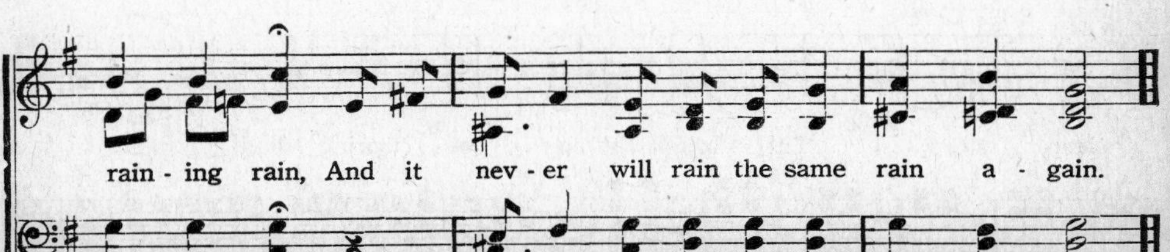
rain - ing rain, And it nev - er will rain the same rain a - gain.

168 Under the Snow.

ALICE JEAN CLEATOR. (P.) MAURICE A. CLIFTON.

1. Un - der the snow so white and deep, Dear lit - tle flow'rs are fast a - sleep,—
2. Soon shall the rain with joy - ful sound Tap at the door- ways of the ground,
3. Then all ar- rayed in col - ors bright, Beau - ti - ful flow'rs shall greet the sight,—
Hid - den all safe - ly from the storm, Un - der a blan - ket white and warm.
Call - ing: "O lit - tle flow'rs a - rise, Sun-shine is gleam-ing in the skies."
Dear sum- mer flow'rs long hid - den low, Un - der a shin - ing robe of snow.
CHORUS.
Sleep, lit - tle flow - ers, sleep 'neath the snow,...... Till bright the
sun of spring shall glow;...... Sleep, soft - ly sleep,...... sleep,
sleep, sleep,...... Till bright the sun of spring shall glow!......
pp
f

Comrades of the King.

169

G. L. H. (J.) GRACE L. HOSMER.

1. O hear our voic - es ring, We're com - rades of the King, And while we fol - low in His way Our march - ing song we sing.
2. We la - bor for the right, Our strength is in His might, And true we ev - er strive to be, And loy - al in His sight.
3. A - lone we nev - er stand, For al - ways near at hand We have a Cap - tain kind and brave To cheer His march - ing band.
4. We own a weap - on strong, One sure to con - quer wrong, The love of Christ for all the world, And this our march - ing song:
CHORUS.
On, on, on, come our tramp-ing feet; For - ward we are march - ing, nev - er to re - treat. On, on, on, sing, in tri-umph, sing! We are comrades of the King......................

170 Blessed Saviour.

E. E. HEWITT. (J.) I. OFFENBACH.
Arr. by ALFRED JUDSON.

1. Bless - ed Sav - iour, meek and low - ly, Sweet the gos - pel sto - ry;
2. Bless - ed Sav - iour, stay be - side us, Till we see Thy glo - ry;
Son of God and King most ho - ly, Lord of life and light;.........
Thro' life's man - y chang - es guide us, Grant a - bund - ant grace;.........
Ser- aphs sing in star - ry splen-dor Of Thy pow'r and glo - ry, We our
Grace to help a need - y neigh-bor, Tell- ing love's sweet sto - ry, Glad - ly
joy - ous praise would ren-der, Trust-ing in Thy might.......
in Thy fields to la - bor, Till we see Thy face.........
REFRAIN.
Bless - ed Sav - iour,
Lord of Glo - ry, Keep us in Thy care, Guard from ev - 'ry sin,

Blessed Saviour.

Help us vic-t'ry win, While with joy we sing To praise our King.

Dear Lord and Father of Mankind. 171

(J.)

JOHN G. WHITTIER. FREDERICK C. MAKER.

1. Dear Lord and Fa - ther of man - kind, For - give our fev - 'rish
2. In sim - ple trust like theirs who heard, Be - side the Syr - ian
3. O Sab - bath rest by Gal - i - lee! O calm of hills a -
4. Drop thy still dews of qui - et - ness, Till all our striv - ings

ways; Re - clothe us in our right - ful mind; In pur - er
sea, The gra - cious call - ing of the Lord, Let us, like
bove! Where Je - sus knelt to share with thee The si - lence
cease; Take from our souls the strain and stress, And let our

lives thy serv - ice find, In deep - er rev - 'rence, praise.
them, with - out a word, Rise up and fol - low Thee.
of e - ter - ni - ty, In - ter - pret - ed by love.
or - dered lives con - fess The beau - ty of Thy peace. A - men.

172 With Happy Voices Singing.
WILLIAM G. TARRANT.
(J.)
BERTHOLD TOURS.
1. With hap-py voic-es sing-ing, Thy chil-dren, Lord, ap-pear; Their joy-ous prais-es bring-ing In an-thems full and clear. For skies of gold-en splen-dor, For az-ure roll-ing sea, For blossoms sweet and ten-der, O Lord, we wor-ship Thee.
2. For tho' no eye be-holds Thee, No hand Thy touch may feel, Thy u-niverse un-folds Thee, Thy star-ry heavens re-veal. The earth and all its glo-ry, Our homes and all we love, Tell forth the wondrous sto-ry Of One who reigns a-bove.
3. And shall we not a-dore Thee, With more than joy-ous song, And live in truth be-fore Thee, All beau-ti-ful and strong? Lord, bless our souls' endeav-or Thy serv-ants true to be, And thro' all life, for-ev-er, To live our praise to Thee. A-men.
173 Rejoice, Ye Pure in Heart.
EDWARD A. PLUMPTRE.
(J.)
ARTHUR H. MESSITER.
1. Re-joice, ye pure in heart, Re-joice, give thanks and sing;
2. Bright youth and snow-crown'd age, Strong men and maid-ens fair,
3. With voice as full and strong As o-cean's surg-ing praise,
4. Yes, on thro' life's long path, Still chant-ing as ye go;
5. Still lift your stan-dard high, Still march in firm ar-ray,

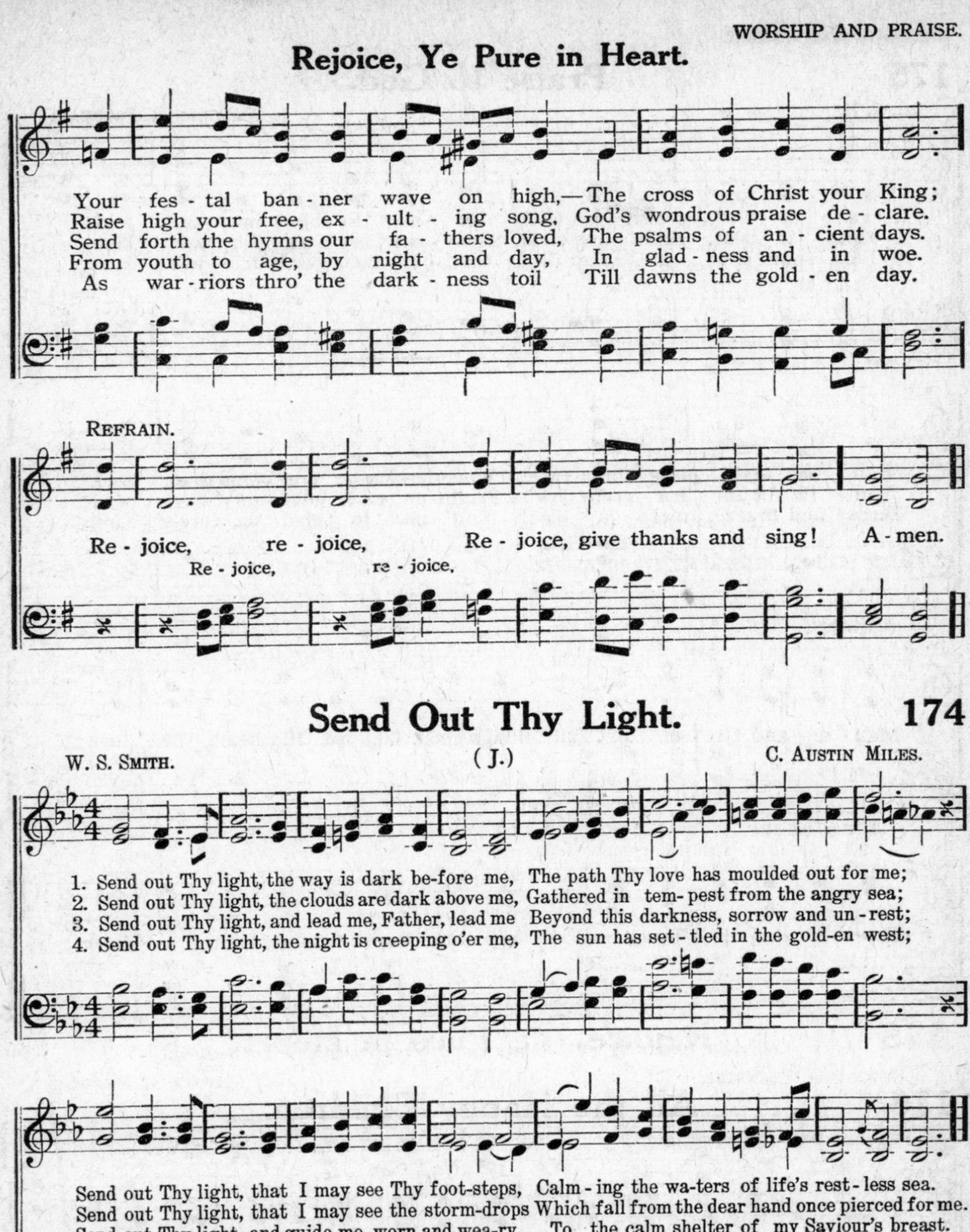
Rejoice, Ye Pure in Heart.
Your fes - tal ban - ner wave on high,—The cross of Christ your King;
Raise high your free, ex - ult - ing song, God's wondrous praise de - clare.
Send forth the hymns our fa - thers loved, The psalms of an - cient days.
From youth to age, by night and day, In glad - ness and in woe.
As war - riors thro' the dark - ness toil Till dawns the gold - en day.
REFRAIN.
Re - joice, re - joice, Re - joice, give thanks and sing! A - men.
Re - joice, re - joice,
Send Out Thy Light.
174
W. S. SMITH.
(J.)
C. AUSTIN MILES.
1. Send out Thy light, the way is dark be-fore me, The path Thy love has moulded out for me;
2. Send out Thy light, the clouds are dark above me, Gathered in tem-pest from the angry sea;
3. Send out Thy light, and lead me, Father, lead me Beyond this darkness, sorrow and un-rest;
4. Send out Thy light, the night is creeping o'er me, The sun has set-tled in the gold-en west;
Send out Thy light, that I may see Thy foot-steps, Calm-ing the wa-ters of life's rest-less sea.
Send out Thy light, that I may see the storm-drops Which fall from the dear hand once pierced for me.
Send out Thy light, and guide me, worn and wea-ry, To the calm shelter of my Saviour's breast.
Send out Thy light, O bless-ed Saviour bring me In the glad morn to Thy dear land of rest.

175 Praise to God.

C. R. F. (J.) CAROLYN R. FREEMAN.

1. Praise to God, praise to God, For all His bless-ings un - told;
2. God is near, skies are clear, Heav - ens are ra - diant and blue,
3. Blos - soms gay all the day, Glad - ly their sweet trib - ute bring;
Beau - ties fair, pleas - ures rare, Won - ders more pre - cious than gold.
Sun - lit hours, fra - grant flow'rs, Bright - en each gold - en day new.
Birds and breeze, mel - o - dies Sing un - to glad na - ture's King.
CHORUS.
Mak - er and Giv - er of all things good, Out of His heart of love;
Free - ly each bless-ing does God be - stow, Praise the dear Lord a - bove.

176 All the Happy Children.

FRANCES BENT DILLINGHAM. (P.) Adapted from MOZART.

1. All the hap - py chil - dren Glad - ly join our song, Ris - ing to the
2. See the sky a - bove us, Spread so warm and blue; So God's love is
3. All the hap - py chil - dren Thank Thee, Fa - ther dear, For this day for

All the Happy Children

Fa - ther, In a cho - rus strong. Birds are bright-ly sing - ing,
reach - ing O - ver me and you. Fa - ther dear, we thank Thee
chil - dren Out of all the year. We will still re - mem - ber
Leaves are opening wide, Flow - er bells are ring - ing Forth on ev - 'ry side.
For long sum-mer days, For the birds and flow - ers, For the grass-y ways.
We are Thine a - lone; He who made the sum - mer Made us ev - 'ry one.
Hosanna! Be the Children's Song.
177
JAMES MONTGOMERY.
(J.)
LUDWIG VAN BEETHOVEN.
1. Ho - san - na! Be the chil - dren's song To Christ, the chil - dren's King;
2. Ho - san - na! Sound from hill to hill, And spread from plain to plain;
3. Ho - san - na! On the wings of light O'er earth and o - cean fly;
4. Ho - san - na! Then, our song shall be, Ho - san - na to our King!
His praise, to whom their souls be - long, Let all the chil - dren sing.
While, loud - er, sweet - er, clear - er still, Woods ech - o to the strain.
Till morn to eve, and noon to night, And heav'n to earth re - ply.
This is the chil-dren's ju - bi - lee: Let all the chil - dren sing. A-men.

178 All For Jesus.

GRACE GORDON. (B–P.) ARTHUR WILTON.

1. Lit - tle hands for Je - sus, There is work to do, Lit - tle tasks so low - ly, Just for me, for you.
2. Lit - tle hearts for Je - sus, Just for Him a - lone, For He loves the chil - dren, Seeks them for His own.

REFRAIN.

All we have for Je - sus, All to Him we bring; We may be His help - ers, We may serve our King.

179 O God, I Thank Thee For Each Sight.

CAROLINE A. MASON. (J.) HERBERT S. IRONS.

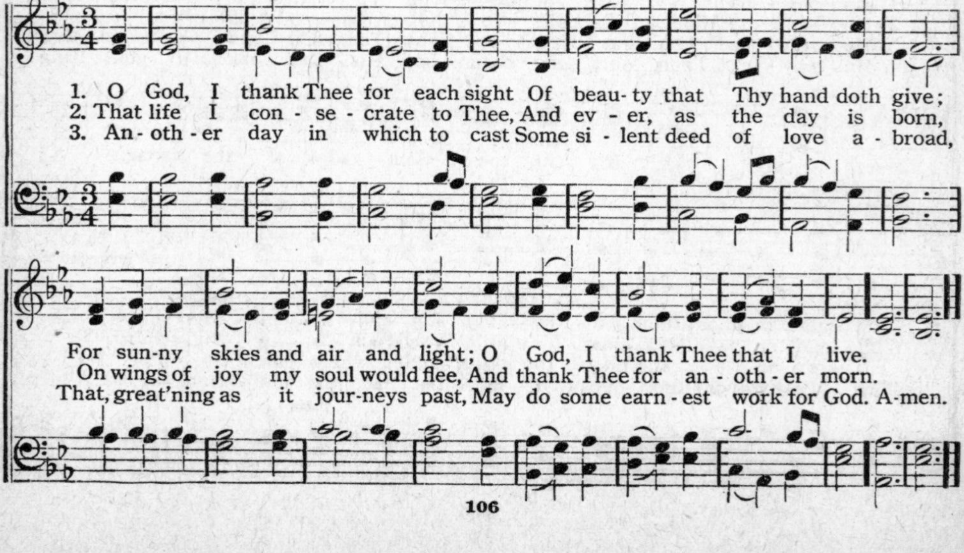

1. O God, I thank Thee for each sight Of beau - ty that Thy hand doth give; For sun-ny skies and air and light; O God, I thank Thee that I live.
2. That life I con - se - crate to Thee, And ev - er, as the day is born, On wings of joy my soul would flee, And thank Thee for an - oth - er morn.
3. An - oth - er day in which to cast Some si - lent deed of love a - broad, That, great'ning as it jour-neys past, May do some earn - est work for God. A-men.

Marching With the Heroes.
180
(J.)
William George Tarrant.
Adam Geibel.
Unison.
1. Marching with the he - roes, Comrades of the strong, Lift we hearts and voic - es As we march a - long; O the joy - ful mu - sic All in cho - rus raise! Theirs the song of triumph, Ours the song of praise.
2. Glo - ry to the he - roes, Who in days of old Trod the path of du - ty, Faith-ful, wise and bold, For the right un - flinch - ing, Strong the weak to save, War-riors all and freemen, Fighting for the slave.
3. So we sing the sto - ry Of the brave and true, Till a - mong the he - roes We are he - roes, too; Loy - al to our Cap - tain Like the men of yore, Marching with the he - roes On-ward ev - er - more.
Refrain. Parts.
March - ing with the he - roes, Com - rades of the strong,
March - ing, march - ing,
Lift we hearts and voic - es As we march a - long.

181 The Song of the New Crusade.

Lizzie DeArmond.
(J.)
Adam Geibel.
Unison.
1. We come, we come like the hosts of old to triumph o - ver sin, The Sun-day School, in an army strong, the world for Christ to win.
2. We come, we come by the will of God, the Lamp of Truth we bear, Till shines the light of the gos-pel ray in glo - ry ev-'ry-where;
3. We come, we come in a might-y band His cross up-lift- ed high, Our feet keep time to the glad refrain that floods the sunlit sky.
Semi-Chorus. ad lib.
We'll onward press at the Master's call, in arm - or bright arrayed, Our voic-es ring in a joyous strain—the song of the "New Cru-sade."
With Zion's King as our Lead-er true, we ne'er can be dismay'd, But praise His name, as we shout and sing the
We forward march at the trumpet's call, our hearts on Christ are stay'd, While loud and clear sounds the music sweet, the
Full Chorus.
Forward, press forward, forev-er, Forward! With hearts un-dis-may'd, Forward! The world for Jesus, The song of the "New Crusade."

In the Garden. 182

C. A. M. — C. Austin Miles.

Slowly.
1. I come to the gar-den a - lone, While the dew is still on the ros - es; And the voice I hear, Fall-ing on my ear; The Son of God dis-clos - es
2. He speaks, and the sound of His voice Is so sweet the birds hush their singing And the mel - o - dy, That He gave to me; With - in my heart is ring - ing.
3. I'd stay in the garden with Him Tho' the night around me be fall - ing, But He bids me go; Thro' the voice of woe, His voice to me is call - ing.
Chorus.
And He walks with me, and He talks with me, And He tells me I am His own,
And the joy we share as we tar - ry there, None oth - er has ev - er known.

Gloria Patri. 183

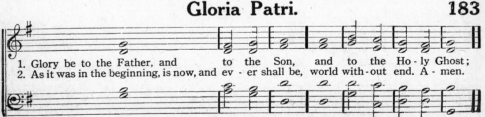

1. Glory be to the Father, and to the Son, and to the Ho - ly Ghost;
2. As it was in the beginning, is now, and ev - er shall be, world with-out end. A - men.

184 Jesus Came.

ELSIE DUNCAN YALE. (B.) CLYDE WILLARD.

185 Birthday Song.

C. A. M. (B–P.) C. AUSTIN MILES.

Jesus came from heav'n above, Christmas morn; Little children, tell His love, Christmas morn.
REFRAIN.
1
2
Christmas morn, Christmas morn, Day when Christ was born; Day when Christ was born.
Copyright, MCMXXIX, by Hall-Mack Co. International Copyright Secured.
Someone has a birth-day, Who can it be? Will you put your hand up
D.S.—So that we may give you
FINE.
D.S. al Fine.
After Fine.
So all may see? Now, will you tell us, How old you are. A hap-py birth-
This sil-ver star.*
day, A hap-py birth-day, With pleas-ure we wish you A hap-py birth-day.

* A silver star may be pasted upon a Birthday Card.

There's a Song in the Air. 186

JOSIAH G. HOLLAND. (J.) C. AUSTIN MILES.

1. There's a song in the air! There's a star in the sky! There's a moth-er's deep
2. There's a tu - mult of joy o'er the won-der - ful birth, For the Vir-gin's sweet
3. In the light of that star lie the a - ges impearled; And that song from a -
4. We re - joice in the light, and we ech - o the song That comes down thro' the
pray'r, and a Ba - by's low cry! And the star rains its fire while the
Boy is the Lord of the earth. Ay! the star rains its fire while the
far has swept o - ver the world. Ev - 'ry hearth is a - flame, and the
night from the heav - en - ly throng. Ay! We shout to the love - ly e -
beau - ti - ful sing, For the man - ger of Beth - le - hem cra - dles a
beau - ti - ful sing, For the man - ger of Beth - le - hem cra - dles a
beau - ti - ful sing, In the homes of the na - tions, that Je - sus is
van - gel they bring, And we greet in His cra - dle our Sav - iour and
King! For the man - ger of Beth - le - hem cra - dles a King!
King! For the man - ger of Beth - le - hem cra - dles a King!
King! In the homes of the na - tions, that Je - sus is King!
King! And we greet in His cra - dle our Sav - iour and King! A - men.

187 Christ was Once a Little Baby.
Lavinia E. Brauff.
(P.)
Florence W. Williams.
Not too quickly.
1. Christ was once a lit - tle Ba - by Just like you and me,
Born in Beth - le - hem of Ju - dah, Far a - cross the sea;
No room for the lit - tle Je - sus Could be found on earth;
And a sta - ble dark and drear - y Was His place of birth.........
2. Day by day the lit - tle Je - sus Grew like you and me,
Learn'd to lisp a pray'r to heav - en At His moth - er's knee;
He was poor, but ver - y hap - py, Hap - py in God's love,
List - 'ning to His gen - tle guid - ance Com - ing from a - bove.........
3. This is still the same dear Je - sus Of whose birth we sing;
O 'tis sweet to tell the sto - ry Of our new - born King,
Who was once a lit - tle Ba - by Just like you and me,
Born in Beth - le - hem of Ju - dah, Far a - cross the sea...........
Copyright, MCMXXIX, by Hall-Mack Co. Renewal.
188 Glory to God.
A. A. P.
(P-J.)
A. A. Payn.
What was the song of the an - gels to shep - herds on Ju - de - a's plain?
Copyright, MCMXXIX, by Hall-Mack Co. International Copyright Secured.
Note.—Teacher may sing or recite the question as music is played.

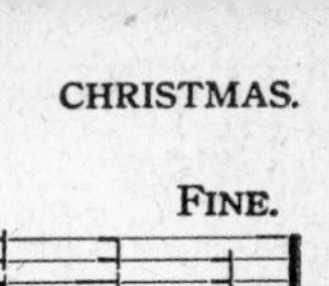

Glory to God.

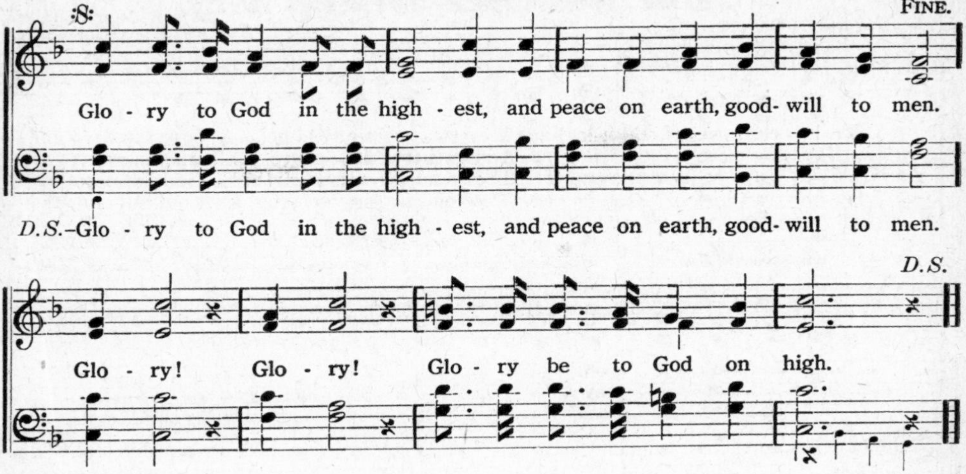

FINE.

Glo - ry to God in the high - est, and peace on earth, good- will to men.

D.S.–Glo - ry to God in the high - est, and peace on earth, good- will to men.

D.S.

Glo - ry! Glo - ry! Glo - ry be to God on high.

Luther's Cradle Hymn. 189

M. L. (B–P.) MARTIN LUTHER.

1. A - way in a man - ger, No crib for a bed, The lit - tle Lord Je - sus Laid down His sweet head; The stars in the sky Looked down where He lay,— The lit - tle Lord Je - sus, A - sleep in the hay.
2. The cat - tle are low - ing, The poor Ba - by wakes, But lit - tle Lord Je - sus, No cry - ing He makes; I love Thee, Lord Je - sus! Look down from the sky, And stay by my cra - dle, To watch lul - la - by.

190 O Little Town of Bethlehem.

PHILIPS BROOKS. LEWIS H. REDNER.

1. O lit - tle town of Beth-le- hem, How still we see thee lie; A- bove thy deep and
2. For Christ is born of Ma - ry; And gathered all above, While mortals sleep, the
3. How si - lent - ly, how si - lent- ly, The wondrous gift is giv'n! So God im-parts to
4. O ho - ly Child of Beth-le- hem, De-scend to us we pray; Cast out our sin and

dream-less sleep The si - lent stars go by: Yet in thy dark streets shin- eth The
an - gels keep Their watch of wond'ring love. O morn-ing stars, to - geth - er Pro-
hu - man hearts The bless-ings of His heav'n. No ear may hear His com - ing, But
en - ter in; Be born in us to - day. We hear the Christ mas an - gels The

ev - er- last-ing Light; The hopes and fears of all the years Are met in thee to - night.
claim the ho-ly birth; And prais-es sing to God the King, And peace to men on earth.
in this world of sin, Where meek souls will receive Him still, The dear Christ enters in.
great glad tidings tell; O come to us, a - bide with us, Our Lord Emman- u - el.

191 We Three Kings of Orient.

JOHN H. HOPKINS. JOHN H. HOPKINS.

1. We three kings of O - ri-ent are; Bearing gifts we traverse a - far, Field and fountain
2. Born a King on Bethlehem plain, Gold I bring to crown Him again King for - ev - er
3. Frankin-cense to of-fer have I; Incense owns a De - i-ty nigh: Pray'r and praising
4. Myrrh is mine; its bit-ter perfume Breathes a life of gathering gloom; Sorrowing, sighing,
5. Glorious now behold Him a - rise King, and God, and Sac - ri - fice, Al - le - lu - ia,

We Three Kings of Orient.
Refrain,
moor and mountain Following yonder star.
ceas-ing nev-er O-ver us all to reign.
all men raising, Worship Him, God on high.
bleeding, dying Seal'd in the stone-cold tomb.
al-le-lu-ia! Heaven and earth replies.
O star of wonder, star of night; Star with
roy-al beau-ty bright; Westward leading, still proceeding, Guide us to Thy perfect light.
The First Noel.
192
Traditional.
Traditional Melody.
1. The first No-el the angels did say Was to certain poor shepherds in fields as they lay;
2. They look-ed up and saw a Star Bright in the East be-yond them far,
3. And by the light of that same Star, Three Wise Men came from coun-try far;
4. Then en-tered in those Wise Men three, Full rev-'rent-ly up-on the knee,
In fields where they lay keeping their sheep, On a cold winter's night that was so deep.
And to the earth it gave great light, And so it continued both day and night.
To seek for a King was their in-tent, And to follow the Star wher-ev-er it went.
And of-fered there, in His pres-ence, Their gold, and myrrh and frankincense.
Refrain.
No-el, No-el, No-el, No-el, Born is the King of Is-ra-el.

CHRISTMAS.
193 Sleep, My Little Jesus.
WILLIAM C. GANNETT.
(P–J.)
ADAM GEIBEL.
UNISON.
1. Sleep, my little Je - sus, On Thy bed of hay, While the shepherds homeward Journey on their way. Moth- er is Thy shepherd And will her vig - il keep: Did the voic - es wake Thee? O sleep, my Jesus, sleep!
2. Sleep, my little Je - sus, While Thou art my own! Ox and ass Thy neighbors, Shalt Thou have a throne? Will they call me bless - ed? Shall I stand and weep? Be it far, Je - ho - vah! O sleep, my Jesus, sleep!
3. Sleep, my little Je - sus, Wonder-ba - by mine! Well the singing an - gels Greet Thee as di - vine. Thro' my heart, as heav - en Low the ech - oes sweep Of glo - ry to Je - ho - vah! O sleep, my Jesus, sleep!
REFRAIN.
Soft - ly sleep, sweetly sleep, My Je - sus, sleep!
Adam Geibel Music Co., owners of copyright. Assigned to Hall-Mack Co.
194 Fairest Lord Jesus.
(P–J.)
Arr. by RICHARD S. WILLIS.
1. Fair-est Lord Je - sus! Rul - er of all na - ture! O Thou of God and man the Son! Thee will I cher - ish, Thee will I hon - or, Thee, my soul's glory, joy, and crown.
2. Fair are the meadows, Fairer still the woodlands, Robed in the blooming garb of spring; Je - sus is fair - er, Je - sus is pur - er, Who makes the woeful heart to sing.
3. Fair is the sunshine, Fairer still the moonlight, And all the twinkling star - ry host; Je - sus shines brighter, Je - sus shines pur - er Than all the an - gels heav'n can boast.
116

Silent Night! Holy Night! 195

JOSEPH MOHR.
FRANZ GRUBER.
1. Si-lent night! Ho-ly night! All is calm, all is bright! 'Round yon vir - gin mother and Child!
2. Si-lent night! Ho-ly night! Shepherds quake at the sight, Glories stream from heaven a - far,
3. Si-lent night! Ho-ly night! Son of God, love's pure light, Radiant beams from Thy ho-ly face,
Ho - ly Infant so tender and mild, Sleep in heaven-ly peace, Sleep in heaven-ly peace.
heav'nly hosts sing Al - le-lu - ia, Christ the Saviour is born, Christ the Saviour is born!
with the dawn of redeem-ing grace, Je- sus, Lord, at Thy birth, Je - sus, Lord, at Thy birth.
Joy to the World. 196
ISAAC WATTS.
Arr. from HANDEL.
1. Joy to the world! The Lord is come; Let earth re - ceive her King; Let
2. Joy to the world! The Sav - iour reigns; Let men their songs em - ploy; While
3. No more let sin and sor - row grow, Nor thorns in - fest the ground; He
4. He rules the world with truth and grace, And makes the na - tions prove The
ev - 'ry heart pre-pare Him room, And heav'n and na - ture sing, And
fields and floods, rocks, hills and plains, Re - peat the sound-ing joy, Re-
comes to make His bless-ings flow Far as the curse is found, Far
glo - ries of His right-eous - ness, And won-ders of His love, And
1. And heav'n, and heav'n and na - ture
heav'n and na - ture sing, And heav'n, and heav'n and na - ture sing.
peat the sound - ing joy, Re - peat, re - peat the sound-ing joy.
as the curse is found, Far as, far as the curse is found.
won - ders of His love, And won-ders, and won - ders of His love.
sing,
sing, And heav'n and na - ture sing,

197 Hosanna, Loud Hosanna.
JEANNETTE THRELFALL. (P–J.) HENRY SMART.
1. Ho - san - na! Loud ho - san - na! The lit - tle children sang; Thro' pillared court and tem - ple The glo-rious anthem rang: To Je - sus who had blessed them, Close folded to His breast, The chil-dren sang their praises, The sim-plest and the best.
2. Fair leaves of sil - v'ry ol - ive They strew'd upon the ground, Whilst Salem's circling mountains Ech - oed the joy-ful sound; The Lord of men and an - gels Rode on in low - ly state, Nor scorn'd that lit-tle chil-dren Should on His bid-ding wait.
3. "Ho - san - na in the high-est!" That ancient song we sing; For Christ is our Re - deem - er, The Lord of heav'n our King. O may we ev - er praise Him With heart and life, and voice, And in His bliss-ful pres-ence E - ter - nal - ly re - joice. A - men.
198 Children's Easter Praise.
(B.) Air from MENDELSSOHN.
On this bless - ed Eas - ter day, Lit - tle chil - dren sing
Joy - ful songs of love and praise, Un - to Christ, the heaven - ly King.

Christ the Lord is Risen To-day. 199

CHARLES WESLEY. LYRA DAVIDICA.

1. Christ the Lord is ris'n to - day, Al - - le - lu - ia! Sons of men and an - gels say; Al - - le - lu - ia! Raise your joys and tri - umphs high, Al - - le - lu - ia! Sing, ye heav'ns, and earth reply, Al - - le - lu - ia!

2 Vain the stone, the watch, the seal;
Christ has burst the gates of hell:
Death in vain forbids Him rise;
Christ has opened Paradise.

3 Soar we now where Christ has led,
Following our exalted head:
Made like Him, like Him we rise;
Ours the cross, the grave, the skies.

The Strife is O'er, the Battle Done. 200

Anon. (Latin.) Trans. by Rev. FRANCIS POTT. Arr. from GIOVANNI P. DA PALESTRINA.

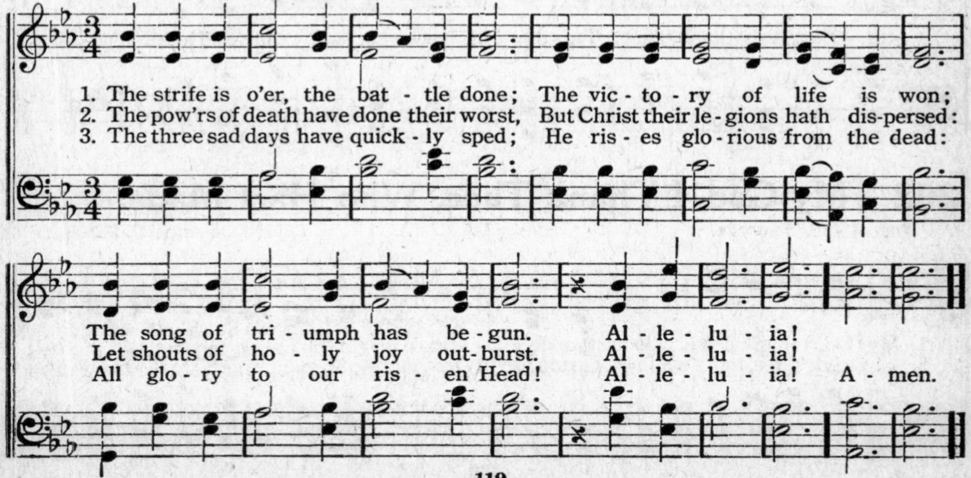
1. The strife is o'er, the bat - tle done; The vic - to - ry of life is won;
2. The pow'rs of death have done their worst, But Christ their le - gions hath dis - persed:
3. The three sad days have quick - ly sped; He ris - es glo - rious from the dead:
The song of tri - umph has be - gun. Al - le - lu - ia!
Let shouts of ho - ly joy out - burst. Al - le - lu - ia!
All glo - ry to our ris - en Head! Al - le - lu - ia! A - men.

201 Can a Little Child, Like Me?
Mary Mapes Dodge.
(P.)
W. K. Bassford.
1. Can a lit - tle child, like me, Thank the Fa - ther fit - ting - ly? Yes, O yes, be good and true, Pa - tient, kind, in all you do; Love the Lord, and do your part; Learn to say with all your heart.
2. For the fruit up - on the tree, For the birds that sing of Thee, For the earth in beau - ty dressed, Fa - ther, moth - er, and the rest, For Thy pre - cious, lov - ing care, For Thy boun - ty ev - 'ry - where.
3. For our com - rades and our plays, And our hap - py hol - i - days, For the joy - ful work and true That a lit - tle child may do, For our lives but just be - gun, For the great gift of Thy Son.
Refrain.
Fa - ther, we thank Thee, Fa - ther, we thank Thee, Fa - ther in heav - en, we thank Thee. A - men.
202 My God, I Thank Thee, Who Hast Made.
Adelaide A. Procter.
(J.)
Frederick C. Maker.
1. My God, I thank Thee, who hast made The earth so bright, So full of splendor and of joy,
2. I thank Thee, too, that Thou hast made Joy to abound; So man - y gen - tle tho'ts and deeds

My God, I Thank Thee, Who Hast Made.

Beau - ty and light; So man - y glorious things are here, No - ble and right.
Cir - cling us round, That in the dark-est spot of earth Some love is found. A-men.
Come, Ye Thankful People, Come.
203
Altered by HUGH HARTSHORNE.
(J.)
GEORGE I. ELVEY.
1. Come, ye thank - ful peo - ple, come, Raise the song of har - vest-home;
2. All the bless-ings of the field, All the stores the gar - dens yield;
3. These to Thee, our God, we owe, Source whence all our bless - ings flow;
All is safe - ly gath - ered in, Ere the win - ter storms be - gin;
All the fruits in full sup - ply, Rip - ened 'neath the sum - mer sky;
And for these our souls shall raise Grate - ful vows and sol - emn praise.
God, our Mak - er, doth pro - vide, For our wants to be sup - plied;
All that spring with boun-teous hand Scat - ters o'er the smil - ing land;
Come, then, thank - ful peo - ple, come, Raise the song of har - vest - home;
Come to God's own tem - ple, come, Raise the song of har - vest-home.
All that lib - 'ral au - tumn pours From her rich o'er-flow - ing stores:
Come to God's own tem - ple, come, Raise the song of har - vest- home. A- men.

204 Christ Has Need of You.
GRACE GORDON.
(J.)
CLYDE WILLARD.
1. Christ has need of work - ers, Faith - ful, loy - al, true! Keep - ing close be - side Him, He has need of you!
2. Christ has need of help - ers, Will - ing, eag - er too! Glad to do His bid - ding, He has need of you!
3. Christ has need of reap - ers, Work - ers are but few, Fields are white with har - vest, He has need of you!
CHORUS.
Serve Him, serve Him! Glad His task to do! Serve Him, serve Him! He has need of you!
Copyright, MCMXXIX, by Hall-Mack Co. International Copyright Secured.
205 Hymn of Thanks.
(P.)
MYLES B. FOSTER.
1. For my home and friends I thank Thee, For my Fa - ther, moth - er, dear, For the hills, the trees, the flow - ers, And the sky so bright and clear.
2. Those I love Thou wilt watch o - ver, Tho' they may be far a - way, For Thou lov - est lit - tle chil - dren, And wilt hear the words they say.

My Country, 'Tis of Thee. 206
S. F. Smith.
Henry Carey.
1. My coun-try! 'Tis of thee, Sweet land of lib - er - ty, Of thee I sing: Land where my
2. My na - tive coun-try, thee, Land of the no - ble, free, Thy name I love; I love thy
3. Let music swell the breeze, And ring from all the trees, Sweet freedom's song; Let mor-tal
4. Our fa-ther's God, to Thee, Author of lib - er - ty, To Thee we sing: Long may our
fathers died! Land of the pilgrim's pride! From ev'ry mountain side Let freedom ring.
rocks and rills, Thy woods and templed hills: My heart with rapture thrills Like that above.
tongues awake, Let all that breathe partake; Let rocks their silence break, The sound prolong.
land be bright, With freedom's holy light; Protect us by Thy might, Great God, our King.
America the Beautiful. 207
Katherine Lee Bates.
Samuel A. Ward.
1. O beau- ti - ful for spacious skies, For am- ber waves of grain, For pur-ple mountain
2. O beau- ti - ful for pilgrim feet, Whose stern impassioned stress A thoroughfare for
3. O beau- ti - ful for patriot dream That sees beyond the years Thine al - a - bas - ter
maj - es- ties A - bove the fruit-ed plain! A-mer - i - ca! A-mer - i - ca! God
free-dom beat, A - cross the wil - der - ness! A-mer - i - ca! A-mer - i - ca! God
cit - ies gleam, Undimmed by hu-man tears! A-mer - i - ca! A-mer - i - ca! God
shed His grace on thee, And crown thy good with brotherhood From sea to shining sea!
mend thine ev-'ry flaw, Conform thy soul in self con-trol, Thy lib - er - ty in law!
shed His grace on thee, And crown thy good with brotherhood From sea to shining sea!

208 How Betsy Made the Flag.

C. A. M. (P-J.) C. AUSTIN MILES.

1. Said Washing-ton to Bet-sy Ross, "A flag our na-tion needs, To lead our val-iant sol-diers on to high and no-ble deeds; Now, can you make one for us?" To which she made re-ply "I am not cer-tain that I can; at least I'll glad-ly try."
2. Said Bet-sy Ross to Wash-ing-ton, "Your country's flag behold," And thro' his tear-dimmed eyes he saw the Stars and Stripes unfold; Then to his breast he clasped it and looked to heav'n a-bove, "O may it ev-er stand" he cried, "for right and truth and love."
3. She made the flag as we all know with stitches strong and neat, And nei-ther on the land or sea has that flag met de-feat; The Stars and Stripes shall ev-er a-bove our coun-try wave, Our land of truth and free-dom and the home-land of the brave.

CHORUS. *Slower.*

So she took some red for the blood they shed, Some white for puri-ty, Some stars so bright from the sky o'erhead, Some blue for loyal-ty, And sewed them all to-geth-er, For

NOTE. This is sung with great success using the following exercise: A flag lying on a table is concealed. Before it are heaps of red, white and blue paper, and also irregular pieces of white paper representing stars. While singing refrain, drop portions of the paper upon the flag and as refrain after third stanza is ended wave the flag.

rit.
loy - al hearts and true ; And hand in hand as one we stand, For the red, white and blue.
God Gave Me Dear America.
209
C. R. F.
(P.)
Carolyn R. Freeman.
1. God gave me dear A - mer - i - ca, The home-land of the free,
2. No oth - er flag can be more bright, No oth - er land more fair;
3. God gave me dear A - mer - i - ca, And thus I will re - pay;
Where lit - tle chil - dren all may dwell In peace and lib - er - ty.
And count - less are the gifts she gives Her chil - dren ev' - ry - where.
For - ev - er will I hon - or her; Her laws I will o - bey.
Chorus.
I pledge my [1]heart, I pledge my [2]hand, To [3]God and to my [4]na - tive land;
To both of them I will be true, For that is what I ought to do.

1. Lay right hand on heart. 2. Extend hand. 3. Gesture upward. 4. Gesture to flag, if one is handy. Otherwise gesture outward. Hold Gesture.

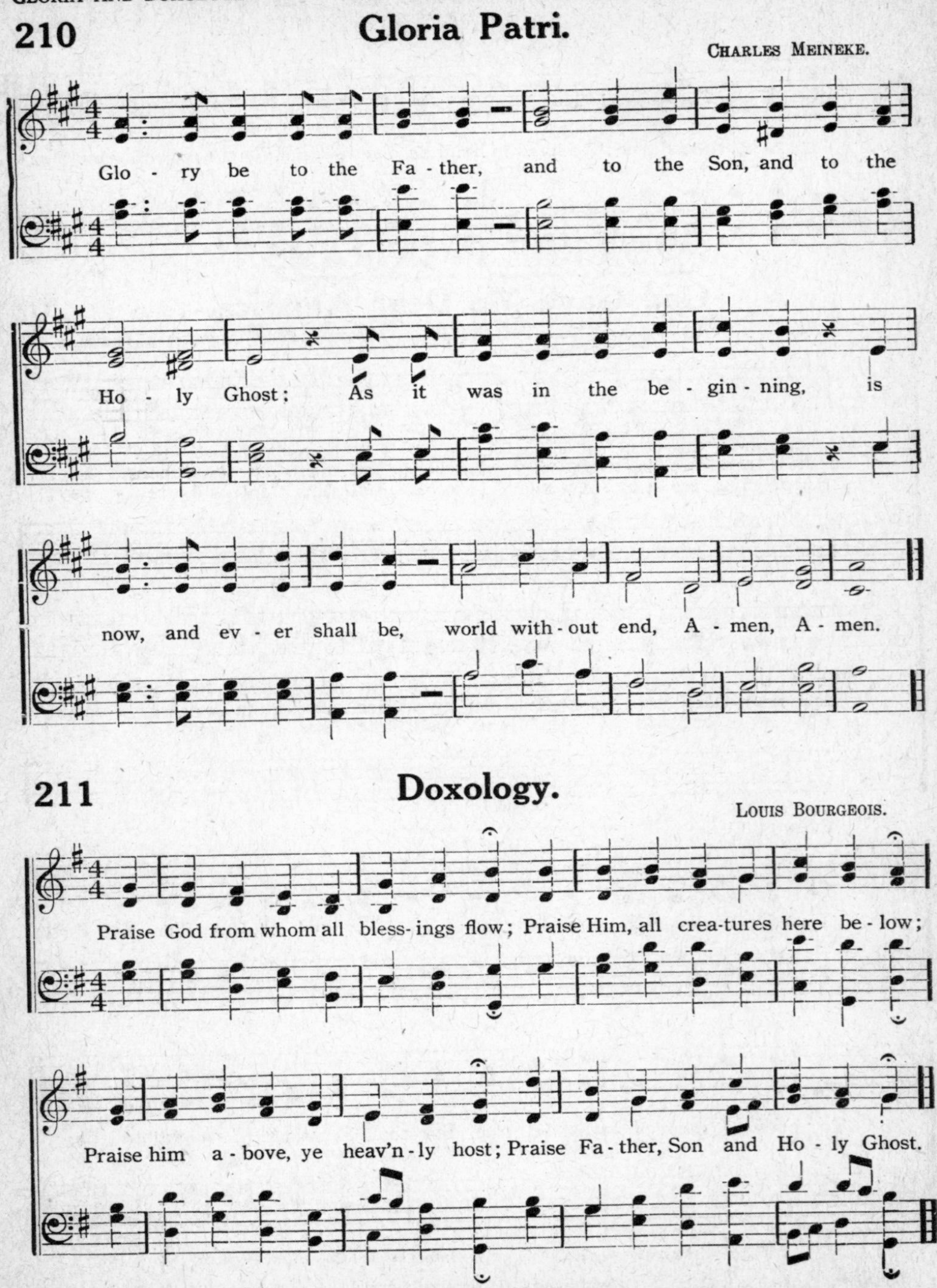
210
Gloria Patri.
CHARLES MEINEKE.
Glo - ry be to the Fa - ther, and to the Son, and to the
Ho - ly Ghost; As it was in the be - gin - ning, is
now, and ev - er shall be, world with - out end, A - men, A - men.
211
Doxology.
LOUIS BOURGEOIS.
Praise God from whom all bless - ings flow; Praise Him, all crea - tures here be - low;
Praise him a - bove, ye heav'n - ly host; Praise Fa - ther, Son and Ho - ly Ghost.

WORSHIP PROGRAMS

OUR CHILDREN AT WORSHIP

THESE worship services are offered as suggestions of what is appropriate for beginners, primary children and junior boys and girls. It is, however, well to remind ourselves that no worship material, even though it be well graded, will lead the children to worship, unless they have the right idea of the God they worship. If they conceive God to be a loving Father, kind, protective, helping them, strengthening them, ready to respond to every thought of Him or call to Him, they will praise Him and pray to Him in a joyous, worshipful mood. Such a God inspires love and devotion.

These worship services may be used as they appear by some teachers. Others may desire to use only certain sections of them, inserting the selected portions into the regular order of service at appropriate places.

Maud Junkin Baldwin, B.R.E.

Mrs. Baldwin is the author of Programs I-XII.

Programs XIII, XIV, XV were prepared especially for this book by Miss Lillian E. Reed.

WORSHIP PROGRAM NO. I

Theme: God's Care for His Children.

Aim: To impress the fact that God always cares for all His children.

Pictures: Cut pictures from magazines showing children eating food, with warm clothing, enjoying companionship with parents. Mount them carefully and place over them the words, "The Lord is Good to all."

1. **The Call to Worship:**
   Use the music of "This is the Day," No. 1.

2. **Hymn:** Sing "This is the Day."

3. **Scripture:**

   LEADER: There is a verse in the Bible which tells us from whence come all our beautiful gifts. Do you remember it?

   CHILDREN: "Every good and perfect gift is from above, coming down from the Father." James 1:17.

   LEADER: God's gifts help us to know Him as our Heavenly Father. When we speak to Him we say:

   CHILDREN: "O God, Thou art our Father." Isaiah 64:8.

   LEADER: Tell me some of the gifts of the Father which you enjoy most.

   CHILDREN: Name the gifts including food, clothing, home, parents, etc.

   LEADER: These are all good gifts, but God gave us one best gift. Tell me about it.

   CHILDREN: "God so loved the world that he gave His only begotten son." John 3:16.

4. **Prayer:**
   Dear Heavenly Father, we thank Thee for every good gift—food, home, clothing, parents. Help us to show our love and thanks by obeying Thy commands. Amen.

   LEADER: Since our Heavenly Father gives us so much, let us lovingly bring our gifts to Him.

5. **Prayer:**
   Dear Father, our off'rings we bring Thee,
   And ask for a blessing today,
   Without Thee our gifts can do little,
   O make them of service, we pray.

6. **Hymn:** "It's Just Like God the Father," No. 68.

WORSHIP PROGRAM NO. II

Theme: Jesus' Love for Children.

Aim: To emphasize the fact that Jesus loves children and wants them to love Him.

1. **Call to Worship:**
   Music of "Jesus Loves Me," No. 88

2. **Hymn:** "Jesus Loves Me."

3. **Scripture:** Mark 10:13-16. Repeated by the leader.

4. **Prayer:**
   LEADER (with children repeating each phrase in concert): Dear Lord Jesus, we thank Thee for Thy love. Help us to remember every day that Thou dost care for us. Make us obedient and true to Thee at home, at school and at play. Amen.

5. **Hymn:** No. 98, "I've Found a Friend."

6. **Offering Service:**
   Tell the pupils that many children have not yet heard of Jesus' love for them. Explain how part of the money they bring to the Church school is used to tell others about Jesus

7. **Hymn:** No. 110, "Saviour Teach Me."

8. **Prayer:** All join in reverently praying the Lord's Prayer.

WORSHIP PROGRAM NO. III

Theme: Loving and serving our country.

Aim: To deepen the children's love for our country and create in them a desire to serve it every day they live.

1. **The Call to Worship:**
   Music of "America," No. 206.

2. **Hymn:**
   Sing "America."

3. **Scripture:**
   Leader: Blessed is the nation whose God is the Lord. Psalm 33:12.

   Children: Seek ye first the kingdom of God, and all things shall be added unto thee. Matt. 6:33.

4. **Selected poem or story.**

5. **Conversation:**
   In regard to the meaning given by some people to the colors of our flag. The red is for courage, the white is for purity and the blue for truth. It is a fact that only those children who are courageous in right doing, who keep their minds and bodies pure in thought and word and deed, who speak the truth at all times are really true to the country for which the flag stands.

6. **Salute to the United States Flag:**
   Let the children rise at the piano signal and salute the flag:

   "I pledge allegiance to the flag of the United States of America, and to the Republic for which it stands; one nation, indivisible, with liberty and justice for all."

   Salute to the Christian flag:

   LEADER: The reason our country has been great in the past is because her leaders loved and obeyed God through Jesus Christ, our Lord. For this reason let us pledge ourselves to His service as we salute the Christian flag:

   "I pledge allegiance to the Christian flag, and to the Saviour for whose kingdom it stands; one brotherhood uniting all mankind in service and in love."

7. **Prayer:**
   Dear Heavenly Father, we thank Thee for our great country. Help us to love her and to serve her by being obedient to Thee and by being kind to all our neighbors, near and far. Amen.

8. **Hymn No. 207,** "America the Beautiful."

9. **Offering Service:**
   LEADER: Many children in our own land do not know how to love and to serve our country in the best way, because they do not know the Heavenly Father. Let us bring our gifts to buy Bibles to send to them or to pay a teacher to tell them about Him.

   Offering Present: Hymn No. 152, "We Give Thee But Thine Own."

10. **Doxology.**

WORSHIP PROGRAM NO. IV
MISSIONS

Theme: God Loves the Children in All Lands.

Aim: To help the children understand that God is the loving Heavenly Father of all children everywhere.

1. **Prelude:** Music No. 142, "O Zion, Haste."

2. **Call to Worship:** Hymn selected from No. 139 to 145.

3. **Scripture:** Repeat from memory:
   "Love one another as I have loved you." John 15:12.
   "Be ye kind one to another." Ephesians 4:32.
   "Suffer the little children to come unto me." Mark 10:14.

4. **Prayer:**
   Dear Heavenly Father, we thank Thee that all little children everywhere belong to Thee, those who are nearby and those who are far away across the sea; those who are white and those who are black, brown, red or yellow. Help us to be kind and helpful to them all. Amen.

5. **Picture Story:** Show suitable pictures, and tell how Jesus came to bring the message of God's love to the children of all races.

6. **Song:** "The World Children for Jesus," No. 139.

7. **Offering Service:** We can help children who do not know the Heavenly Father by sending missionaries and Bibles to them. It takes money, too, for this work. Let us give of what God has given us to help them.

8. **Hymn:** "Little Children Far Away," No. 143.

   Prayer: Dear Heavenly Father, bless our offering of love. May it help many children to learn about Jesus. Amen.

9. **Closing Hymn—The Doxology.**

WORSHIP PROGRAM NO. V

Theme: The Easter Story.

Aim: To help the children feel something of the hidden meaning of all the new life in springtime, and prepare them for appreciation of the Easter message.

Objects: Lily bulb and lily in bloom.

1. **Greetings:**

   Happy Easter to you,
   Happy Easter to you,
   Happy Easter, dear friends,
   Happy Easter to you.

   Sing to the tune of No. 16.

2. **The Call to Worship:** Music of Children's Easter Praise, No. 198.

3. **Hymn:** Children's Easter Praise.

4. **Conversation:** Talk about the flowers and seeds which have been sleeping all winter under the warm earth with a white blanket of snow in the colder countries. Tell how they are waiting for the voice of God to call them to new life, and how that voice comes to them by means of the soft breezes, the warm sunshine, and the gentle spring rain.

5. **Story:** Show the lily bulb and tell a simple story of how a bulb like

this went to sleep in the soft, dark earth last autumn and how God called to it in the early spring.

Describe the appearance one by one of the green leaves, and finally of the lily itself. Show the plant.

6. **Prayer:** Our Father, we thank Thee for all the waking flowers and leafing trees. Amen.

7. **Second Story:** One day some cruel men who did not love our wonderful friend, Jesus, planned to take away His life. They hurt Him so much that His life was gone, so they took His body and placed it in a cave and rolled a stone before it. But they were mistaken, for after three days Jesus appeared to His friends many times and proved to them that He was alive for evermore. They were so glad, just as glad as we are today, and they sang praises to Christ. Let us sing to Him.

8. **Hymn No. 23.**

9. **Offering.**

NOTE: Send to your "Book Room" for "Easter Helper," which contains plenty of material for Easter.

WORSHIP PROGRAM NO. VI

Theme: The Message of the Risen Lord: "Because I live ye shall live also."

Aim: To use the new life at springtime to help the children appreciate somewhat the hope we have of an immortal life through Jesus Christ, our Lord.

1. **Prelude:** "Spring Song," Mendelssohn, or other instrumental selection.

2. **Call to Worship:**

   For, lo, the winter is past,
   The snow is over and gone,
   The flowers appear on the earth,
   The time of the singing birds has come.
   Song of Solomon 2:11.

3. **Song:** No. 51, "All Things Great and Wonderful."

4. **Prayer** (children repeating after leader):

   We thank Thee, dear Heavenly Father, for the beautiful world in which we live. We thank Thee for Thy loving care that has made the world so beautiful. We thank Thee for the springtime and the flowers, the birds, the blue sky, and the bright sunshine. We thank Thee for Jesus who loved the flowers and the birds, and who lives in heaven today to help and bless us. Amen.

5. **Story:** Bible Story, Mark 16:1-7, or John 20:11-18.

6. **Hymn:** "In the Garden," No. 182.

7. **Offering:** No. 150. Music during offering; then sing.

   Prayer:

   Jesus, bless the gifts we bring Thee,
   Give them something sweet to do,
   May they help some one to love Thee,
   May we love Thee, too. Amen.

8. **Closing Music:** No. 199, "Christ the Lord is Risen Today."

WORSHIP PROGRAM NO. VII

Theme: God the Giver of all things.
(For general use. May be adapted to New Year, Birthday, etc.)

Aim: To help the children think of God, the Father, when they enjoy their daily blessings of home, food, clothing.

Pictures: Cut from magazines and mount pictures of homes, parents caring for children, food, children singing praises. Place where children may easily see them.

1. **Greetings:** (Stand and sing)
   "Good Morning to You," No. 16.
   A Happy New Year (or birthday)
   A Happy New Year (or birthday)
   With pleasure we wish you
   A Happy New Year (or birthday)
2. **The Call to Worship:**
   Music of "This is God's House," No. 28.
3. **Hymn:** Sentence No. 23.
4. **Story:**
   The Baby Moses Cared For. Ex. 2:1-10.
5. **Brief Conversation** about the comfort of homes and warm clothing in winter for children, feathers for birds, fur for animals.
6. **Prayer:** Repeat words only or sing No. 106.
7. **Offering:**
   Let some child bring the offering basket to the center of the circle or any other appointed place. Teacher reads words of No. 151. Then as the music is played the offering is received.
8. **Hymn:** "Praise Him," No. 19.

Note: For Birthday, see Hymn 185.

WORSHIP PROGRAM NO. VIII

Theme: Children Thanking God.

Aim: To help the children express their thanks to God in a way natural to them.

1. **Greetings:** "Good Morning to You," No. 16.
2. **The Call to Worship:**
   Music No. 28, "This is God's House." Music played first then words sung softly and reverently.
3. **Scripture:**
   Leader: The Heavenly Father has given us the sun and the moon and stars to light our way by day and by night. He has made the earth beautiful, too, all that we might be happy and glad. Do you remember a verse in God's Word which tells us about His goodness?
   Children: "The Lord is good to all." Ps. 145:9.
   Leader: "I will give thee thanks with my whole heart." Ps. 138:1.
4. **Song:** No. 11, "O Give Thanks."
5. **Story:** David: From Shepherd boy to King. His thanksgiving. Chron. 29-13.
6. **Prayer:** Words of No. 23 recited and sung.
7. **Hymn No. 19.**

WORSHIP PROGRAM NO. IX

Theme: Little Children Serving God.

Aim: To show the children how they may serve God.

Materials: Make a large red heart. On it paste pictures of children rendering some loving service.

WORSHIP PROGRAMS

1. **Greetings:** "Good morning to you."
2. **The Call to Worship:** Music played first and then the words sung. "This Is God's House," No. 5.
3. **Hymn:** "Jesus Bids Us Shine," No. 89.
4. **Prayer:** Words only of "Lord Who Lovest Little Children," No. 112.
5. **Story:**
   "Samuel Helping in God's House," in the Bible.
6. **Hymn:** No. 22 (Use "Serve Him").
7. **Offering:**
8. **Hymn:** No. 48, "Good-Bye Song."

WORSHIP PROGRAM NO. X

Theme: Celebrating Jesus' Birthday.

Aim: To teach that Christmas is the day we observe Jesus' birthday; to stimulate feelings of love for God and for the Baby Messiah; to show the children the true way to celebrate Christmas.

1. **Prelude:** Music of No. 196, "Joy to the World."
2. **Hymn:** No. 184, "Jesus Came."
3. **Conversation:**
   Show pictures of the birth of Jesus. Let the children talk about the loveliness of a baby. Say, God sent the baby Jesus because he loved us. Then converse about their own gifts to others. Emphasize the thought of sharing with others because God says, "Love one another," and because He has shown us how to give.
4. **Prayer:**
   LEADER: Dear Heavenly Father, we thank Thee for the Baby Jesus. Help us to show our love for Him by loving others. In Jesus' name. Amen.
5. **Story:**
   Bible Story, Luke 2:8-20.
6. **Hymn:** No. 187, "Christ Was Once a Little Baby."
7. **Offering.**
   After the offering is presented let the leader pray:
   Father in Heaven, Thou didst send Thy son to make us happy. We give this money to make others happy. We pray Thee to accept our offering. In Jesus' name. Amen.
8. **Hymn:** "Away in a Manger," No. 189.

WORSHIP PROGRAM NO. XI

Theme: Little Children Loving Jesus.

Aim: To give children opportunity to show their love for Jesus.

1. **Quiet music:** "Jesus Loves Me," No. 88.
2. **Song:** "Jesus Loves Me," first stanza, or chorus only.
3. **Scripture:**
   LEADER: Jesus said, "Suffer little children to come unto me." Mark 10:14.
   CHILDREN: We love Him because He first loved us. 1 John 4:19.

4. **Story:** Jesus Loving Little Children. Mark 10:13-16.

5. **Prayer** followed by words of No. 20.

6. **Picture:** Show "The Triumphal Entry," (Plockhorst), and tell how the children showed their love for Jesus by waving palm branches and singing, "Hosanna to the Son of David."

7. **Hymn:** No. 25.

8. **Offering:** Jesus said, If you love me and want to show that love for Me, do something for My little children who need food or clothes. So we shall bring our offerings now and send them to help little ones who have no one to care for them.

Prayer:

"Jesus bless the gifts we bring Thee,
Give them something sweet to do,
May they help some one to love Thee,
May we love Thee, too. Amen."

9. **Closing Song:** "Good-bye Song," No. 48.

WORSHIP PROGRAM NO. XII

Theme: The Christian Life.

Aim: To arouse appreciation of the body as God's temple; to lead the pupils to decide upon habits of purity and self control.

1. **Prelude:** Music of No. 73.

2. **Hymn:** "Father, Lead Me," No. 73.

3. **Scripture Responses:**

LEADER: As you know, each of us is born with a body and a spirit. We can see the body but the spirit which is its life we cannot see. The spirit lives in the body and depends on the body to express its love, its joy, its unselfishness, its kindness. Our spirits need good bodies for this work. What does God's word say about taking care of our bodies?

PUPILS: Know ye not that ye are the temple of God and that the spirit of God dwelleth in you? If any man defile the temple of God, him shall God destroy; for the temple of God is holy, which temple ye are. 1 Cor. 3:16, 17.

LEADER: How can we take the right care of our bodies?

PUPILS: Whether, therefore, ye eat, or drink, or whatsoever ye do, do all to the glory of God. 1 Cor. 10:31.

LEADER: There are some good rules in regard to eating and drinking in the Bible. Can you repeat two?

PUPILS: Eat in due season for strength. Eccl. 10:17. Look not on the wine when it is red. Prov. 23:30, 31.

4. **Story:**

A Clean Life follows clean acts, which follow clean thoughts, which follow clean desires, which spring from the source of all good—God, the Father, through Jesus, his Son, who should be youth's ideal. Or,—God the Father, revealed by Jesus the Son, our example, who inspires purity of thought, desire, word and act resulting in a clean life.

5. **Hymn:** No. 128.

6. **Offering:**

After it is presented let the leader pray and let the pupils repeat in concert the phrases one by one:

Our Father in heaven, we desire at this time to present not only these gifts of money to Thee, but to give Thee our bodies to be used as Thy messengers. Let our hands and feet and tongues be used to serve Thee. In Jesus' name. Amen.

Hymn: No. 106, "To Think and Do Right."

7. **Pledge:** Close with this pledge memorized by all the Juniors:

I am resolved to live
  A life of purity;
For my example I will take
  The Christ of Calvary.
To live as pure as he
  Shall ever be my aim,
That I may no dishonor bring
  Upon his or my name.

Hymn: No. 125, "O Master, When Thou Callest."

JUNIOR WORSHIP PROGRAM NO. XIII

Theme: "Christian Activity."

Prelude: No. 148 (may be used).

Opening Sentence in Unison: "Be ye doers of the word and not hearers only."

Hymn: "Father Lead Me," No. 73 **(first** verse only).

Father lead me day by day
Ever in Thy righteous way;
Teach me to be pure and true,
Show me what I ought to do.

Chorus of Juniors: "To Think and Do Right," No. 106.

(Second verse No. 73.)

When in danger make me brave,
Make me know that thou canst save;
Keep me ever by thy side,
Let me in thy love abide.

Response by Junior: Psalm 91:1-2.

He that dwelleth in the secret place of the Most High shall abide under the shadow of the Almighty. I will say of Jehovah, He is my refuge and my fortress; My God in whom I trust.

(Third verse No. 73).

When I'm tempted to do wrong
Make me steadfast, wise and strong:
And when all alone, I stand,
Shield me with Thy mighty hand.
Amen.

Response by a Junior: Psalm 37:23-24.

A man's goings are established of Jehovah;
And he delighteth in his way.
Though he fall, he shall not be utterly cast down; for Jehovah upholdeth him with his hand.

Prayer Song: "Saviour, Teach Me Day by Day," No. 110.

Offering: (taken as an act of worship).

Offering Prayer:

"Dear Jesus our offerings we bring Thee
And ask for Thy blessing today;
Without Thee our gifts can do little,
Oh, make them of service, we pray."[1]
Amen.

Story: "Mock."[2]

Hymn: "We Are Building," No. 115 (sung softly.)

Recessional to classes.

([1] Prayers for Children, by Dietz.)

([2] "Rules of the Game," by Lambertson.)

JUNIOR WORSHIP PROGRAM NO. XIV

Theme: "Happiness."

Prelude: No. 114 (played softly).

Call to Worship: "This is the Day Which the Lord Hath Made," No. 17.

Prayer:

Our Father help us to be happy
And strong at home, in school,
At play, in church and to be like
Jesus who taught us to pray—
"Our Father who art in heaven",

Hymn: "Rejoice, Ye Pure in Heart," No. 173.

Recitation of Psalm 100 by a Junior.

SUPT.: Blessed are the poor in spirit;

RESPONSE: For Theirs is the kingdom of heaven.

SUPT.: Blessed are they that mourn;

RESPONSE: For they shall be comforted.

SUPT.: Blessed are the meek;

RESPONSE: For they shall inherit the earth.

SUPT.: Blessed are they that hunger and thirst after righteousness;

RESPONSE: For they shall be filled.

SUPT.: Blessed are the merciful;

RESPONSE: For they shall obtain mercy.

SUPT.: Blessed are the pure in heart;

RESPONSE: For they shall see God.

SUPT.: Blessed are the peacemakers;

RESPONSE: For they shall be called the sons of God.

SUPT.: Blessed are they that have been persecuted for righteousness sake;

RESPONSE: For theirs is the kingdom of heaven.

SUPT.: Blessed are ye when men shall reproach you, and persecute you and say all manner of evil against you falsely, for my sake;

RESPONSE: Rejoice and be exceedingly glad, for great is your reward in heaven; for so persecuted they the prophets that were before you.

Chorus of Juniors: "With Happy Voices Singing," No. 172.

Offering: (Taken as an act of worship).

Response: Jesus, to Thee Our Offering, No. 150.

Story: "The Magic Mask."[1]

Recessional to classes.

([1] "Ethics for Children," by Cabot.)

JUNIOR WORSHIP PROGRAM NO. XV

Theme: "Thankfulness."

Prelude: No. 94 (played softly).

Call to Worship: "O Give Thanks Unto the Lord," No. 11.

Hymn: No. 202, "My God I Thank Thee, Who Hast Made."

Responsive Reading:

SUPT.: "It is a good thing to give thanks unto Jehovah."

RESPONSE: "I will give thanks unto Jehovah with my whole heart."

SUPT.: "Because he hath set his love upon me."

RESPONSE: "Therefore I will give thanks unto Jehovah and tell of all thy wondrous works."

SUPT.: "Jehovah will hear me when I call."

RESPONSE: "I will give thanks unto Jehovah according to his righteousness."

ALL: "Great is thy loving kindness toward me and I will behave myself wisely and in a perfect way."[1]

Hymn: No. 179, "O God, I Thank Thee for Each Sight."

Offering: (taken as an act of worship).

Response 152: "We Give Thee But Thine Own."

Story: "What Bradley Owed"[2] or "The Ungrateful Self."[3]

Prayer:

We thank Thee for playmates, companions, friends,
For all the good things, the Father sends,
We thank Thee for the happy hours at play
And for the hours at school each day.
We thank Thee for Thy love, so strong so true.
We thank Thee for parents and strength to do.
The little kindnesses which express our gratitude,
We pray Thee keep us in health and grace
And may we always be faithful in every place.
Amen.

Response: Selection 20.

Recessional to classes.

([1] Taken from the Psalm, American Revised Version.)

([2]—[3] Found in Manual for Training in Worship, Hartshorne.)

INDEX.

(*The figures refer to the hymn number, not to the page.*)

A

A Morning Prayer 109
A Prayer 131
All for Jesus 178
All the Happy Children 176
All Things Bright and Beautiful 56
All Things Great and Wonderful 51
America the Beautiful 207
An Even-Song 69

B

Blessed Saviour 170
Bless the Lord, O My Soul 2
Bless Us and Keep Us 39
Birthday Song 185
Boys and Girls of Every Color 141

C

Call to Worship 12
Can a Little Child Like Me? 201
Children's Easter Praise 198
Children in the Temple 10
Christ Has Need of You 204
Christ the Lord is Risen To-day 199
Christ was Once a Little Baby 187
Come Unto Me 129
Comrades of the King 169
Come, Ye Thankful People, Come 203

D

Day is Done 40
Day is Dying in the West 44
Dear Lord and Father of Mankind 171
Doing Our Best 123
Do Something for Somebody 122
Doxology 211

E

Enter into His Gates 104

F

Fairest Lord Jesus 194
Faith of Our Fathers 146
Father, Hear Us when We Pray 18
Father in Heaven 9
Father, Lead Me 73
Father, Lead Me Day by Day 113
Father, We Thank Thee 108
Fling Out the Banner! Let it Float 144
Flowers 162
Follow Me 81
For God So Loved the World 72
For Jesus 134
For the Beauty of the Earth 57
For Us, His Children 75
From Greenland's Icy Mountains 145

G

Gentle Saviour, God of Love 4
Give, Said the Little Stream 149
God is Everywhere .... 50 and 55
God Gave Me Dear America 209
God Knows What is Best for You 165
God is Great and Good 54
God is Love 77
God is Near 74
God of the Whole Wide World 60
God that Made the Earth and Heaven... 42
God will Take Care of Us All 135
God's Care 157
Gloria Patri .... 183 and 210
Glory to God 188
Golden Rule Song 120
Good-Bye and God Be with You 43
Good-Bye Hymn 41
Good-Bye Song 48
Good-Morning to All 16

H

He Prayeth Best Who Loveth Best 103
He'll Not Forget His Little Ones 76
His Helpers 121
His Little Ones 100
Holy Bible, Word Divine 65
Holy, Holy, Holy 6
Holy Spirit, Faithful Guide 153
Holy Spirit, Truth Divine 154
Hosanna! Be the Children's Song 177
Hosanna, Loud Hosanna 197
How Betsy Made the Flag 208
How We Know 49
Hurry, Mr. Clock 138
Hymn of Thanks. (Foster) 205
Hymn of Thanks. (Judson) 107

I

I Love Thy Kingdom, Lord 147
I Think when I Read that Sweet Story... 92
I Would Be a Little Sunbeam 118
In Christ there is No East or West 85
In Our Work and in Our Play 86
In the Garden 182
In the Hour of Trial 111
In the Temple 80
I've Found a Friend 98
It's Just Like God the Father 68

J

Jesus Bids Us Shine 89
Jesus Calls Me 91
Jesus Came 184

INDEX.

Jesus, Friend of Little Children 82
Jesus Loves Me 88
Jesus Loves the Little Children 140
Jesus, Loving Jesus 97
Jesus, the Same! 101
Jesus Thinks of Me 79
Jesus, Thou Our Teacher Be 64
Jesus, to Thee Our Offering 150
Joy to the World 196
Just as I Am, Thine Own to Be 128

L

Let the Words of My Mouth 102
Little Children Far Away 143
Little Eyes 137
Little Flowers of Summertime 166
Little Raindrops 164
Lord, We Come to Thee 130
Lord, Who Lovest Little Children 112
Luther's Cradle Hymn 189

M

Marching with the Heroes 180
My Clock 136
My Country, 'Tis of Thee 206
My God, I Thank Thee, Who Hast Made 202
Morning Praise 3

N

Now the Day is Over 45
No Child is Too Little 93

O

O Christ, the Way, the Truth, the Life... 94
O Come, Let Us Go 15
O Day of Rest and Gladness 8
O Father, Hear My Morning Prayer 105
O Give Thanks Unto the Lord 11
O God, I Thank Thee for Each Sight..... 179
O Jesus, I Have Promised 127
O Little Town of Bethlehem 190
O Master! When Thou Callest 125
O Master-Workman of the Race 83
O What Can Little Hands Do? 116
O Worship the King 58
O Zion, Haste 142
Offertory Sentence 151
One Little Star 160
Only God Can Make a Blossom 52

P

Parting Prayer 39
Praise to God 175

R

Raining 167
Rejoice, Ye Pure in Heart 173
Room for the Little Children 99

S

Saviour, Again to Thy Dear Name 47
Saviour, Teach Me Day by Day 110
Send Out the Light 174
Sentences ....19 to 38
Silent Night! Holy Night! 195
Sleep, My Little Jesus 193
Sun and Rain 163

T

Tell Me the Stories of Jesus 87
The Church's One Foundation 148
The Earth is Hushed in Silence. 7
The Evening Star 156
The Father's Care 70
The First Noel 192
The Golden Key 114
The Holy Word 66
The Lord is in His Holy Temple...13 and 14
The Master's Garden 126
The Months of the Year 159
The Nest 161
The Rainbow 158
The Song of the Book 67
The Song of the New Crusade 181
The Strife is O'er, the Battle Done 200
The World Children for Jesus 139
There's a Song in the Air 186
There's Not a Tint that Paints.....50 and 55
This is God's House 5
This is God's World 53
This is My Father's World 59
This is the Day ....1 and 17
Thy Word Have I Hid in My Heart 62
'Tis Not Far to Jesus 90
To Think and Do Right 106
To Thy Father and Thy Mother 117
To Work for Jesus 133
Twinkle, Twinkle, Little Star 155

U

Under the Snow 168

W

We are Building 115
We are Helpers 119
We Belong to Jesus 95
We Give Thee but Thine Own 152
We Three Kings of Orient 191
We Treasure the Message 84
We'll Follow Christ 78
When Jesus Was a Child 96
When Morning Gilds the Skies 3
When the Dawn is Breaking 71
Who Would Not Love the Bible? 61
Why We are Here 124
With Happy Voices Singing 172
Wonderful Words of Life 63

Y

Yes, the Lord Can Depend On Me 132